WHAT
MATTERED

WHAT
MATTERED

DAVID J.

PLUM BAY PUBLISHING, LLC
NEW YORK, NEW YORK
MORRISTOWN, NEW JERSEY

For permission requests, contact the publisher at the website below:
Plum Bay Publishing, LLC
www.plumbaypublishing.com

Library of Congress Control Number: 2022902741
Paperback ISBN: 978-1-7348848-8-3
eBook ISBN: 979-8-9858564-0-8

Printed in the United States of America
Cover Design: Sonya Dalton
Interior Design: Barbara Aronica
Editor: Sally Fay

CONTENTS

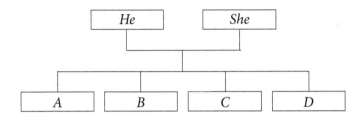

It was their life to screw up,
and he and she had done a masterful job.

Could they, would they, find redemption?

PROLOGUE

A party at the lake. Leaning down, with his arm resting on the frame of the open refrigerator door, he peered in and noticed the bottle of vodka that he had placed next to the milk the night before. He frowned. There was a lot gone. He remembered having had a drink, possibly two. He was certain, though, that it had not been more than that. He had had, to be sure, his occasional moments. All the same, his undoing was food, not drink. As to her, she preferred white wine and rarely drank spirits. Besides, she had committed to him, and to their kids, that she would not drink that day. He decided to let it go.

They were at their Lake house, having arrived the evening before in separate cars from their City house. They were there, along with their two daughters, the younger of their two sons, and their dogs, because they were hosting a party in celebration of the upcoming wedding of the daughter of their next-door neighbors. About 35 people would be attending.

The house was his utopia, the only material possession that had ever meant anything to him. He had long wanted a distraction from his life and work in the city, and he had wanted nothing more than to gaze at an endless expanse of water. She went along with it. They should have been content with what they already had but, at that stage in their lives, they were not the abstemious types. What's more, after many lean years, they were no longer in the mood for restraint.

The house itself was a contemporary, surrounded by two wooded acres on a bluff overlooking the lake and the shale-surfaced beach that was part of the property, and only a two-hour drive from the city. Each of the 10 rooms had an unobstructed view of the water. The asking price was a reach for them though they were successful in securing a substantial reduction. When the seller would go no further, he and she had at best a 30-second conversation about their future, with each stating to the other that their career was on track. They did not get into the what-ifs, or any probative assessment of the sustainability of the purchase over the long haul. They certainly were not contemplating the recession, which was a year or two away.

What of it? After all, it was just a house and, as it could be bought, it could be sold. And so, armed with a hefty second mortgage on their City house, they had at it.

She ordered an assortment of modern furniture—white upholstered, steel, and glass. He did the art. They had reasonably good taste and their pieces, anchored by two large Warhol-like portraits of her that he had commissioned for one of her birthdays, were easy on the eyes. Keeping watch were their two Great Danes, their Doberman, and their Pug.

The sky was clear that morning and the temperature was comfortably warm, with the same forecasted for the evening. She had sent out printed invitations, and had picked up a mountain of flowers and the desserts she had on the occasional times they entertained at the City house. He had arranged for the caterer, selected the food, picked up the wine and other alcohol, had a tent erected in the backyard overlooking the lake, and attended to the range of things that must be done for any party. All was nearly in order, and few last-minute preparations awaited, except for the tables.

For a reason he could not quite discern, she had insisted on buying the tables and chairs that would be placed under the tent where the guests would have dinner. He wanted to rent them. She had her way, showing up two weekends before the party with her vehicle filled with the tables, unassembled and in boxes. He unloaded them and stacked them in one of the garages. She went out again and again, returning with chairs piled one on top of the next in the vehicle. This all introduced a measure of inconvenience as the tables had to be unpacked and assembled. They started the task the weekend before the party, but made scant progress.

On the morning of the party, their 15-year-old daughter (C) took over in earnest. One by one, C assembled the tables, screwing the table legs to the table top, and he and their 20-year-old daughter (B) carried them and the chairs to the lake side of the property and arranged them under the tent. At about the time that the last of the tables was being assembled, she appeared and began to survey the activity. She was immediately accosted by C who pointedly reminded her she was not to drink that evening. That, predictably, did not go over well. All too often, she had stormed out of restaurants or railed at him or the children when she was told she had had enough and could have no more. She would do what she wanted, and that included when, where, and how much she would drink.

As he, B, and C carried the last of the tables and the chairs to the tent, she followed them with her arms crossed against her chest, her hands up, and her two middle fingers extended—with one pointed at B and the other pointed at C. It was not the day or the moment to get into it with her. They opted instead to slip away posthaste, leaving her with her tables and her chairs.

Around noon, he joined her on the outside deck which was accessed from the dining room and which ran along the west side of the house, past the master suite, and to a staircase that descended to the grounds. Certain, after only a few moments of conversation, that she was high, but not sure on what, he decided to ask her about the vodka that had gone missing. She professed to knowing nothing about it and then, stoked by whatever it was that she had consumed that morning, she began to cross-examine him about his suspicions, gesticulating with her index fingers, all the while moving her hands rapidly in every direction. If it was her intent to confuse him, it was not working. If it was his intent to reason with her, it also was not working.

Needing to clear his head, he decided to go for a ride on his bike. He mounted the bike on the rack of his vehicle and took off for a local trail. When he returned an hour or so later, he met with the caterer and some of the wait staff who had arrived to do a preliminary setup. He handled the details, explaining how he wanted things to go that evening. He did not bother to include her. There was no point. What little attention she could muster was directed to the flowers and arranging them in vases to be placed on the tables. Once done with that, she retired to her bedroom and slept for the balance of the afternoon.

By early evening, the house was aglow with the late sun pouring into the rooms. Flowers were all about. The tables that C had uncomplainingly assembled were now covered with white cloths, candles, and flower centerpieces. The bar was stocked, and the caterer and crew were at work on the food and the final preparations. Anxious, but trying to keep calm, he got dressed and he and their 8-year-old son

(D), along with B and C, waited as the guests made their way up the long stretch from the road to the front door.

He went looking for her and found her in her bedroom. It was a large space, accessed by double doors opening from a long corridor of polished black granite that led into, and filled, the room. Panels of glass and sliding glass doors opened to the outside deck and provided commanding views of the lake. In the room, flanking the double doors, were two king-sized beds, one for her and one for him and their dogs. His four-legged soulmate, the fawn Great Dane, was lounging on one of the beds. The close second, his black Great Dane, was sprawled on the other bed. She then made her entrance.

They had met in graduate school. During that time and until they married five years later, she was a brunette who, despite having been an achiever at the fancy prep school and college she had attended, was not particularly sure of herself. Once into the marriage, a metamorphosis began. Over the ensuing years, she shortened her first name, she changed her career, she went very blond and very thin, and she developed a persona that was decidedly edgy. She also became a study in extremes. In her appearance, like the Hollywood stars when they went out without makeup, she could blend in but, when she cared, she was usually the most strikingly good looking and best dressed in the room. The same was true in her work. She had, in one lane, a successful general psychiatry practice and, in the other lane, an equally successful venture for the treatment of sex offenders.

Despite whatever it was she had ingested during the day including, as she admitted to him that afternoon when he had gone to check on her, some vodka in the wee hours of the morning when she could not sleep, she pulled her physical self together. She was in full jewelry, resplendent in a form-fitting turquoise mini-dress and stiletto heels. The shoes pushed her an inch over six feet. Her mental self was another thing. It was apparent to him that she was pretty wasted.

Two years earlier, while she was cleaning up after one of their dogs, she claimed to have hurt her back. After that, she started to complain of spasms. In response, he and the children repeatedly urged her to do something about it. She resisted, just as she resisted other requests by him or one or more of the children that she attend to this or that ailment, or offload this or that item of work that, she avouched, caused her much stress.

It was also about the time he began to notice that she would open her mouth to speak and, while her lips moved, no sound came out. At other times, she could not get or stay up on her own.

One evening, he and C found her crawling along the floor of the lounge on the second level of the City house, unable to stand. They helped her to a chair after which he went down to the first level of the house to read and C went to the third level to study. Moments later, they heard a loud bang, and he and C then raced to where they had left her. Not there, they found her instead flat on her back, partially inside and partially outside the walkway to her bedroom. He and C pulled her by her feet into the room and then lifted her onto the bed. Their attempts to learn what happened were futile. She could not release any audible sound.

Other occasions were less private. The parking attendants at a club where they had dinner with C and D had to carry her to their vehicle because, after too many glasses of wine, she had collapsed in the lobby and could not get up. While on a trip to a neighboring state, after taking in a cabaret show at the hotel where they were staying, it was only by hugging the walls and taking one short step after the next that she could make her way from the elevator to their room.

He would, in a manner, have understood had she been more open about the degree of discomfort and the need to suppress it. Yet, whenever the subject came up, she acted the stoic and unequivocally denied any use, let alone any abuse, of any substance except white wine.

Having visions of another full-on trainwreck, knowing she was a drink or a pill or more into her own party, he alerted B and C and beseeched them to stick by her side.

For a short time that worked. He could see that some of the party guests were making their hellos with her flanked by B and C though, given her condition, attempts at any meaningful conversation were for naught. Later, with more guests arriving and B and C mingling a bit, she was able to break away and secure some wine. Shortly thereafter, their neighbor approached him and motioned toward her. He looked and could see that she was wobbling. A moment later she collapsed and, in her descent, she grabbed for and knocked down one of the paintings.

He, B, and C, as well as the bartender standing nearby, quickly went to where she had landed. Seeing that she could not get up, he went into damage control mode. He decided against taking her to her bedroom on the west side of the house. The guests would, if they looked into the room, be able to see her as they walked along the deck to the exterior staircase and down to the tented area where dinner would be served. So, he had everyone go in the other direction. He and B and C and the bartender carried her down a long hallway to one of the bedrooms on the east side of the house whereupon, after being lifted by the four of them onto the bed, she passed out.

He began to fumble with the elaborate strapping of her shoes in an effort to get them off, and B began to remove some of the jewelry. Meanwhile, C (a tennis star) stood ramrod straight, glaring down at her. C's right forearm and hand moved to a 90-degree angle. C then leaned in and smacked her hard, very hard, across the face. She immediately sprung up with her eyes opening wide and an utterly bewildered look upon her face. Almost in unison, he recoiled—only springing forward when she fell back onto the pillow and passed out again. He then glanced over at C who, with a clenched right fist and a raised right arm to shoulder level, started to go in for a punch. He caught the arm, intercepting the strike.

He managed to get her shoes off, then turned off the lights and shut the door.

B and C, in the intervening time, had gone to the adjacent bedroom. He opened the door to find C curled in a fetal position on the bed, sobbing, and B tucked up in an arm chair, also sobbing. He tried to comfort them but he had many guests, along with D, to attend to and he left the room. He walked down the hallway, and made his way through the house and out to the deck. Descending the stairs, he could see that the guests had taken their places at the tables. He joined D at one of the tables.

On seeing him, their neighbor got up and made a toast to the soon-to-be bride and groom, and to them. He, too, had planned to wish the couple happiness and godspeed as they embarked on married life. He did not get up, though it was his duty and his privilege as the host. It was no excuse, but he was unsettled by what had just occurred and, moreover, what did he know about a happy marriage.

He returned twice to the house to check on her and to try to persuade B and C to join the guests and have some dinner. She remained down and out, and they resolutely declined. Each time, unsuccessful and alone, he returned to the party. On the second try, he paused along the sun deck and gazed out over the lake which was illuminated by the moon. Seeing that and hearing the lively conversations drifting up from the tables, he thought, *"This is really lovely."*

The next morning, he arose early to walk the dogs. When he returned, he noticed that she had packed her things and had placed them next to the front door. They crossed paths, near where she had fallen the evening before and knocked down the painting. She did not speak. Nor did he. She simply gestured toward a white brick ledge that encased the living room fireplace. He knew what she wanted. She had brought some framed photos of the family from the City house and had displayed them on the ledge for the party guests to see. Whether because he knew that they were not the family she was trying to portray or because the frames, though fine for the more traditionally appointed City house, struck him as out of place in the contemporary setting, he had gathered them up before the party and put them in one of the closets. He told her he would bring them back to the City when he, the children, and the dogs returned later that weekend. She hesitated, but then turned and left, without the photos and without saying good-bye to B, C, or D, or to him.

When everyone woke, he took them out for breakfast. Then they went for a long and quiet drive.

WHAT
MATTERED

CHAPTER 1

The First Day of the Revolution

August 27, 2010. Though the timing of it varies, nearly everyone has a breaking point. His came three weeks after the party at their Lake house. Out to dinner with her and intent on getting their lives to a better place, he decided to start with their finances and then ease into her substance issues. He did not get far.

The finances had been her domain ever since, years earlier, he had made the grievous mistake of bouncing a check. She deemed him unfit and took over, ending any real day-to-day or long-term involvement by him. He, thereafter, grew increasingly and imprudently indifferent to matters of money. For a long while, he let himself believe things were secure. She would proclaim that she was so good at it. Only she wasn't. By then, he knew it was bad. The big life, that is to say, how they had lived over the past few years, will do that. So, he told her he was going to reclaim responsibility for that aspect of their affairs. She would have none of it, and whatever it was that was still keeping them together swiftly unraveled.

The drive to their City house from the restaurant took only minutes and neither he nor she spoke. He pulled into the driveway and shut off the ignition. Then, turning to face her and drawing from the toughness he employed when it was needed in his professional life, he spoke to her in a way he never had before. In two short, profanity-laced sentences, he told her he wanted her gone in the morning. He then got out of the car, slammed shut the door, and made his way into the house. He went to the phone and called B who was out with C, D, and their 21-year-old son, A, and insisted that they immediately return to the house. He did not want to be there with her by himself.

Come morning, a Saturday, he retreated or, one might say, escaped to his office. Years before, when he began his career, his colleagues customarily showed up at the office on Saturdays. That became a way of life for him, and continued long after advances in technology and the pursuit of work-life balance thinned the weekend crowd. He had, it was true, a lot of pending work. He always did. Still, it could have waited until Monday. He was there out of habit, and because he did not want to be part of her leave-taking in the event she actually decided to go.

He somewhat doubted she would. Any pushback from him, or from one of the children, or from most anyone else was met with hostility and intransigence. That sort of truculence could have been dealt with in several ways. He largely chose avoidance, and a walking-on-eggshells sort of existence around her.

That Saturday morning, and perhaps because she herself recognized that things could not continue as they were, she did leave. Before doing so, she called him at the office, but she might as well have been talking to herself. He was no longer listening. It was much too late for that.

As soon as she closed the front door and drove off, their children mobilized. It was little wonder. Their home life had been unnecessarily complex until veering, in the last year, to the chaotic.

The complex part came from the choices he and she had made early on in their life together. In the late eighties and only a few years into the marriage, she was fired from her job. Pregnant (with B) and with a toddler (A) at home, she found the job market decidedly grim. They supplemented his income with her unemployment compensation benefits and embarked on what became a protracted challenge to her termination. The benefits expired and, with no job prospects in sight, she decided that she wanted to become a medical doctor. To turn that pipedream into a reality, she went back to school and, for a two-year period, took all of the science classes she never took the first time she was in college. Against the odds, she succeeded and was accepted, early decision, into a top-ranked medical school.

She matriculated at the age of 34. By then, A was just three and B was just two. What followed were four long years of classes, labs, tests, and clinical rotations. What also followed was another pregnancy and the birth of their third child (C) at the start of her fourth year of medical school. Then came four years of internship and residency, including a year as the chief administrative resident at one of the foremost psychiatric hospitals in the country.

For him and his career, it was years on the Daddy Track.

For the children, it was much time spent with nannies. She was understandably busy and not around. And, he, though around and hands-on with them, was the principal source of the family income and could not risk losing a job where, though excelling at the technical aspects, he had been falling steadily behind his peers. He lacked the time to devote to the business development aspects of the job but, truth be told, that wasn't his bag.

The children had, during those years, every right to protest. Whether they did or did not or, if they did, whether anyone heard them, would really not have mattered. They were all too far into their collective support of her becoming a doctor.

The chaotic part came from choices he and she made as they forged a post-medical school, post-residency life. To begin, their fourth child, D, was born. At the same time, and intent on regaining lost ground, he went full throttle at work—except on the weekends when he took over from the nannies and was homebound with the newborn. She, too, binged on work and, also, on white wine. And they each started to acquire more and more things.

His spending was particularly profligate, indeed reckless. He gave little thought to the balances on their credit cards and, if that were not enough, was strangely blind to the inherent sickness of even using a credit card that had a running balance.

By and throughout 2010, the children were crying foul. None of them put a defining label on it and, really, how could they. They just knew that something was very, very wrong.

The less than positive vibe that insinuated itself into their home life derived as well from what she described as her own *"bad obsessive controlling habits."* For him and their children, that was code for an all-about-her and not-about-them mentality which, in the later years, they dubbed *"The She Show."*

Of this time, in a letter to her, B observed: *"You have been an intolerable wife to a good and decent man who has raised four happy and healthy children, supported your career and put up with your self-centeredness for many years at much sacrifice."* C, in an email to him, lamented: *"It is an utter waste of time to even try to discuss important mat-*

ters with her. All she cares about is work. She doesn't care about us." A, fatigued by it all, wrote her: "*You create needless chaos. I'm angry about your self-centeredness and your sense of entitlement. The only thing that matters is building loving relationships with others. You have failed miserably in these areas. Your focus has been on money, career, and things (your stuff)—but for what end?*"

The children's anger could also very rightly have been directed at him. Relationships, whether the political, the familial, or the intimate, need a measure of checks and balances—someone who will step up to the plate and call out or, at the very least temper, unfortunate behavior or decisions. It was not that he was a wimp or could not, as they say, man-up. There were, after all, four children to think about and he did not want to make things even worse for them. Still, in his dealings with her, he could never shake his head-in-the-sand propensities, which helped neither him nor her and only accelerated the downward spiral.

Presented with an opportunity that August morning, the children jumped at it and got to work. In doing so, and to their credit, they chose not to wallow in the past or to spend any inordinate amount of time ruminating about it. They couldn't change it even if they wanted to and, besides, like most trying times, it was not all bad. That morning was about the future.

First up was an easy fix, the purge of her stuff which was symptomatic of some of the chaos. Room by room, in all four levels of the house, they did a clean sweep, and a semblance of order, they said, began to emerge. What also emerged was the certainty that *The She Show,* as they knew it, was over and that it would not be going to syndication. They were tired of making guest appearances and had no stomach for endless nightly reruns.

The four of them then dispatched to a nearby wireless store to change the family cell phone plan. There had been continual chatter amongst them about doing that. The plan was too expensive and no one understood it. But, neither he nor she was paying enough attention. That was a problem in their work-centric way of life and distance from each other. Careers and kids derail many good intentions. For them, there was the additional overlay of denial and then inertia. A fog had drifted in, hazy at first, before it darkened to zero visibility and numbed their remaining senses. That August, whether by luck or by higher intervention, the fog had begun to lift, his consciousness began to return, and there was one last chance for him to ponder how it had gotten to that point and what to do about it.

In many respects, their children were that day simply following a formula that is tried and true. That is to say, most things in this life do, at the end, come down to money, and it was no different for them. They found the checkbook which, later that day, they handed to him, ending her sovereignty over things fiscal. Thanks, as well, to the sagacity of A and B, a budget was drawn, the first in the 24 years of the marriage, and a new era, one of discipline and restraint, along with an imaginable way out, was upon them.

When he returned from the office, he felt relieved that she had left and grateful for their children's good sense. The children had learned, not from him and not from her, but because of him and because of her. They would make wiser decisions, indeed they already had that day, and they would lead more fulfilling and healthier lives for the experience.

Surveying the now decluttered first floor of the house, he entered the dining room with its lofty ceiling, its mahogany woodwork, its dramatic chandelier and crystal-laden wall sconces, and its art. His eyes, though, only fixated on one thing—the dining room table which, with each extension leaf in place, was about 12 feet long. They had purchased the table when they bought the house many years before. They very rarely ate at the table or spent any time as a family in the room. Rather, the table served as her nerve center, where she perched herself on a chair at one end.

As it happened, the floor plan was configured such that the preferred route from the entry gallery to the kitchen was through the dining room. Due to the table's length and where she positioned herself, getting about was never easy. It only worsened when she plugged the cord from her laptop into the wall socket behind the chair where she sat, thereby creating another navigation challenge. Any plea to remove at least one leaf was declined by her. That is how the table, leaves and all, had been arranged by her upon arrival at the house, and that is how the table, leaves and all, would stay.

He approached the table, pulled back the chairs, and bent down to disengage the table's locking mechanisms. Then, with his arms outstretched, he pulled the table apart just enough to remove one of the leaves. Lifting out the leaf and resting it against one of the walls, he pulled the table together, reset the locks, and rearranged the chairs. He slowly moved away from the table and noticed what, in actual fact, had just occurred. A measure of equilibrium had filtered into the room. The table, instead of over-whelming, fit the space.

The final adjustment would not come for another two years when the stager he hired to help him with the sale of the house removed a second leaf from the table, at which point the room came alive. Two years earlier, he did not know any better. He had been so askew for so long that one leaf was a good start.

It was, all considered, a very good start. There was still much to do. There always is, and always will be. Yet, he had done what he had to do and what had been long delayed. She had left, and he and their children were united in the quest for better days. None of them thought much that day as to where it would all lead. They just knew there was no turning back.

In the words of A that evening, it was *"The First Day of the Revolution."*

CHAPTER 2

Crash

Now what? Better is how he would describe the day after the first day, and the day after that, and the day after that. It was, to his eyes, better for their children as well. He did not detect any regret, even as the momentum and thrill of the first day waned. They were not, after all, professional revolutionaries and, come what may, pressing things like getting ready to go back to college, planning for a term abroad, beginning high school, starting fourth grade, working, paying bills, tending to the dogs, working out, spending time with friends, and all of the other business of living diverted their attention from the elephant in the room.

What she was doing or where she was staying, he could not really say. They were no longer speaking to each other. She had also ceased any meaningful contact with B, C, and D, except when she ran into one or the other of them on her infrequent returns to the house to gather an article of clothing or something else that she might need. She turned, instead, to A.

That was probably a good call. Despite all, A had not

yet reached the point of cynicism when it came to her and, in any event, he was a peacekeeper. As to B and C, it is not that they wanted to do battle. It was just that there had been too many promises, empty when made or quickly broken. Ten months earlier, she wrote B: *"I know how much I have disappointed you and I am disgusted with myself. I no longer can bury my troubles in drinking. I have no excuses. I do want to let you know that I have made steps to get better. I am not going to drink at home unless it is allowed by dad and moderated by him in his presence. I am not going to purchase any alcohol. This was a good idea by A that only dad purchase. I owe all of you a healthy sober mother. Please don't give up on me."*

Whether or not she clued him in to his role in her steps to betterment was academic. She would not have allowed him to supervise any aspect of her life, nor was he really equipped to do so. The drinking persisted, enabled or not by him, and the ensuing months brought continued disappointment to B and C. About her, C observed in an email to him: *"She is like a hurricane. She can whip through a house and destroy everything and everyone in it. I cannot even explain how badly she has hurt me."* B, in a note to her, wrote: *"I have really lost all respect for you in the last few years. You have been a terrible mother, wife, colleague and human being. I don't know if you realize the extent to which you have hurt me or your family."*

In daily calls with A throughout the month of September, she steadfastly maintained that she was not drinking. She also steadfastly maintained that the family, not she, was the problem. And that would remain her narrative.

She had, indisputably, a considerable knack aligning others, at least initially, to her way of thinking. Even were she not as adept, she was bound to sway A. One does, at bottom, want to believe and this is particularly so when the speaker is one's mother. With the passing phone conversations, her pleas of victimhood and temperance began to sound genuine to A which, inevitably, weakened the erstwhile solidarity among the other comrades.

He, too, had his narrative. He did not, this late in the day and after years of suppressing his ambition to that of hers, need her censure and spin. And, to the notion that she was living a life of sobriety, he knew otherwise. He deduced this, not because he was spying on her, but because he had taken over the family finances. To help him along, their children had set him up with electronic banking. He could then begin to see, in virtual real time, the ATM transactions. Plus, in the new spirit of financial discipline and restraint, he started at last to become keenly conscious of the flow of money, in and out, and became fixated on what to do about their debts. Through all of this, he could see that she was making purchases at the liquor store.

He, hitherto, had given her the benefit of any doubt. Though largely disengaged from each other, they did, until he asked her to leave, have periodic calls throughout the day. With increasing frequency in the months prior to that point, he often sensed during those calls, mostly the ones in the late afternoon, that she was under the influence of something or other. She would deny it. That would then lead to his calling one or more of the children, and asking them to call her and then call him back with their take. After a few rounds of this, C had enough. Admonishing him, C wrote: "*You are really dealing with this in the wrong way. Time and time again she abuses drugs and alcohol. All you do is collect the facts and give her more opportunities to abuse us. You and I both know that she is defiant and helpless. Until you and she decide to get her some extra help and pain management then nothing is going to change. I am not going to continue living here while you choose to let her mess with our lives. In my eyes you are just as at fault.*"

Whether symptomatic of his passiveness when it came to her or whether, like A, he actually wanted to believe her, he let himself slide into a distorted cycle of "*is she or isn't she?*" C was right. He should not have let that happen. It was, anyhow, a charade. To his question, he knew the answer. For anyone who has been in a relationship for more than a flash, a partner's slight tick or a minor alteration in speech or affect or anything else, all imperceptible to an outsider, will undoubtedly be noted and conclusions drawn irrespective of any overall indifference.

There was bound, at some point, to be a crash. And it did happen. The burn part would, for the moment, wait. The evening of October 6, he received a call at home from her business partner who reported finding her, early in the morning, fully clothed and asleep at her desk, with empty and half-empty wine bottles strewn about. He then received an earful about what life was like at the office with her. Until then, to the extent that he gave it any thought, he was of the view that she was one of the high-functioning types when it came to work. Though other than the pay-checks, he had no evidence. Had he bothered for a second to put money aside and step back, it would not have been a revelation that her decline at home would spill into other spheres of her life.

After he got off the phone, he spent several minutes reflecting. Perhaps this latest had been just another binge, like his food binges, and nothing more. Despite a build-up of troublesome incidents, there had not been a DUI or any of the other truly life-changing consequences of uncon-trolled drinking.

But what, everything considered, was any of this to him? They were living separate and apart, and she had not made any effort to talk reconciliation or to try to work things out. Not that he had.

He reflected a bit longer, and then picked up the phone and dialed directory assistance. Moments later, he was connected to a high-end rehabilitation center, known for treating celebrities, and he began speaking to an intake staff member. He explained why he was calling and then began to describe the conversation he had just had with her business partner and how it came to be that she would be found passed out in her office earlier that day. With a little prompting, and sticking to the events of the previous 12 months, he let loose.

He spoke of the party at the Lake house. He spoke of her stumbles and falls. He spoke of a family trip out of the country when, on the first night, he and C left the hotel suite to take in a light show at the city's landmark and how, the next morning, he and C found a nearly emptied mini-bar with the consumed bottles partially hidden in her effects and elsewhere in the suite. He spoke of a family weekend at a resort and relayed that he, A, B, and C had taken an afternoon excursion with a driver while she remained in their suite with D. He described their calling D to check on things, their being told by D that he could not wake her up, and their immediately turning back to the hotel all the while coaxing D to do everything that he could to rouse her. Continuing, he relayed that D was eventually successful and that, after getting back to the hotel and expressing to her how worried they had been, they let her know she was not welcome to join them for dinner that evening. He then described how C had hid the key to the mini-bar before they left for dinner and that, when they returned from dinner, they found her in bed with the mini-bar opened, the key inserted, and a nail clipper resting on the top of the mini-bar with the fold-out blade broken in half. He described her complaints of back pain and the many times, probably from some sort of self-medication, that she was reduced to gesturing because she was otherwise, through speech, incapable of emitting any understandable words. He went on a bit longer until he was told that it was enough and that, subject to her calling the center and confirming his statements and agreeing to go, she would be admitted.

He then called her and, in a matter-of-fact way, summarized the conversations he had had that evening with her business partner and with the rehabilitation center. He told her that she needed help and, if she would agree, she would fly out to the center for treatment. This time, there was no pushback. She agreed to go and said good night.

No sooner had he put down the phone than, for the first time in his adult life, excepting the births of each of their four children, he began to cry. He could not help it.

She seemed so vulnerable and so unlike the intractable person that, in his mind, she had become.

Later that evening, she sent an email to her business partner, copying him and A, in which she thanked her business partner for "*saving her life.*" Perhaps forgetting her month-long protestations of sobriety to A, she wrote: "*I'd binge and binge and feel sorry for myself in those hotel rooms. It was hard not to binge when I became angry.*" That did not sit well with A. He eventually called her out on it, writing her: "*I was your biggest apologist when you were not living in the house in September. I spoke with you at least 30 minutes a day for four weeks. In that time, you lied to me on numerous occasions and manipulated me into thinking you were the victim. All the while you were pathetically getting loaded every day as an F-you to the family. To find this out was a major blow to me.*"

She returned to their City house to pack for what was to be six weeks of rehabilitation. He drove her to the airport early in the morning, a Sunday, but not early enough. They were late and she missed her flight. She had to be re-routed through two different cities before reaching her destination. He spoke to her during her two layovers and, by the second one, she was incoherent. He did not, this time, call C for her impression.

Most things have a cost and his came as Monday morning rolled around. The center asked for prepayment—over

$30,000. Not having such a sum readily available, he put the charge on one of their credit cards. While he fully expected to recoup a chunk of the payment through an out-of-network claim under his employer's medical plan, he overlooked that he needed her cooperation as well as her authorization for the release of records so that the medical plan could evaluate the claim. When he brought up the need to initiate the paperwork, she quickly shut him down. She voiced concern that, through a claim, it could "*get out*" that she had been in rehabilitation. To his retort that it was already out, she was not swayed. Her answer was no. He would, without her okay, have to eat the cost and he was in no position to do so.

He had only himself to blame for ceding the purse strings to her and, worse, for having foolishly thought that the rapid and significant hike in his income from the time following her completion of her medical residency and his dropping off the Daddy Track meant that he could do what he wanted and purchase what he pleased. He had not foreseen the financial crisis and the huge and irreparable hit that he would take to his income as a result of it, nor had he foreseen potentially ruinous, out-of-pocket rehabilitation costs. There were a lot of rainy days ahead, and nothing put aside.

The treatment charges, added to the already hefty balance on their credit card, generated a staggeringly high monthly interest payment. And that was barely a line item in the debt-ridden state of their financial affairs. It was time to start his own rehabilitation, and he did. Up first was the Lake house, which went on the market. More, much more, would follow.

CHAPTER 3

I Love You More Than Ever

On the surface, it had a Ritz-Carlton feel to it. There was the name and the celebrity aura, the modernistic entrance and manicured grounds, and a former First Lady greeting visitors in the reception area. Then, too, there was the setting in a desert city with breathtaking views of the surrounding mountains. While there, she befriended a film star. While there for what the center called its "*Family Program,*" he befriended the wife of a rock star.

Like many new undertakings, the honeymoon period was promising enough. This she recounted in a series of notes, unaccompanied by any salutation, which she mailed to him in envelopes each bearing her handwritten "*save for my scrapbook.*" Predictably, the period was short-lived. In an email to him, less than two weeks into it, she wrote: "*I want out of here. I also seem to be the one with the most stress, financially and jobwise and the least support. I have received no mail from home and they know I have four children.*" Also short-lived was his willingness to curate her scrapbook. He wrote her: "*No need to send your diary notes home. I know that you are writing them for yourself and your* scrapbook. *Other than being postmarked to me, they don't appear to be any attempt to communicate with me."*

Still, there was headway—at least as to her back complaints. Enrolled in the center's Pain Track, she revealed (after less than two weeks): *"I am pain-free. I have not even taken an Advil in 12 days. No pills at all."* He was not sure what to make of it. He marveled at the quick fix. At the same time, he wondered whether there was really anything to fix. He split the difference, writing her: *"Glad that you appear to be pain-free with the swim therapy, stretching, and yoga. A pity that this was not done a while ago."*

In the early days at the center, the counselor coordinating her treatment obtained her permission to contact him and then contacted him with some regularity. This required that he relive what he was hoping to escape. Gone therefore, at least on this go, was the blissful out-of-sight, out-of-mind stretch that followed his having asked her to move out of their City house in late August. She was now very much on his mind. He wrote her: *"Don't worry about things at home while you are there. Please focus on your own well-being. The time now is to get better."*

Life at the City house had been going smoothly. C was settling into high school, and D was settling into fourth grade. A was back at college, and B was on a quarter abroad. He had his work and, astonishingly, was having the best year of his career. By no means, though, was he paddling alone. There were the two nannies and the housekeeper, and there was the September month-end paycheck from one of her employers. That, along with his compensation for the month, allowed him to pay the two mortgages, the two home equity loans, the interest on two lines of credit, the three car notes, the interest charges on a half-dozen credit cards, the salaries for the household staff, the private school tuition for C, the parochial school tuition for D, the university tuitions for A and B, and the sheer array of day-to-day and other costs necessary to plug the leaks and keep buoyant.

Before long, she had enough of him, not that he much cared, and resumed dealing with him through A. The counselor calls also stopped. He believed that he was being supportive of her and helpful to the counselor. For starters, he had urged her to seek help, he then had facilitated her admission into the center, and he now was saddled with a substantial credit card debt for her treatment. Not so, according to her. She let him know that her counselor found him "*tight*" and had expressed to her that he was treating her "*harshly*" as was the rest of the family. He could have just shrugged it off. What really mattered was that she get better. Yet, he was not about to be the fall guy for her intemperance, nor was he about to have a stranger who knew nothing about him or his life with her cast him as the heavy. He wrote her:

We are none too pleased that your counselor thinks that the family is treating you harshly. We are not. First, she wasn't around and did not live it. More to the point, you don't have a reserve of goodwill. We have borne the brunt of some really nasty and jerky behavior. You have not been affectionate and loving toward A, B, and C (or me—but that is beside the point). Instead, they are called names, have it lorded over them that you somehow work four jobs to support them, and they are given the finger by you. You also have to understand that you lied to us. I don't think in our 29 years of being together, that I knowingly lied to you.

That off his chest, he reverted to a lighter tone: *"All this said, I am hopeful. You have reinvented yourself before and you can absolutely do it again."*

A was receptive to continuing to communicate with her, as no one else was willing, but A was not going to be played again. Staying true to himself, A spoke of the need for compassion in dealing with her. At the same time, A emphasized the importance of not letting her off the hook, observing in an email to him: *"That does not mean we can't remind her about her actions and how angry we are—and remind her we should!"* And she would receive similar reminders. In B's sole communication with her while she was at the center, B wrote: *"I am glad you are finally taking steps to improve your physical, mental, and emotional self. And I hope you are thinking long and hard about the person, mother, and wife you have become."* C refused to engage, her silence being the reminder of the anger that was all about.

Zeroing in on the likelihood of a fail, A wrote him: *"Very disturbing are the stories that sometimes people need 5 or 6 rounds of this before they are 'better.' We don't have the time, money, or inclination to do this."* Knowing, too, his quondam inattention to matters of money, A gave him some advice: *"Strategically speaking we can never rely on her as we once did. So, it would behoove you to become as self-sufficient as possible. You need to be prepared if this doesn't work out."*

At the midway point of her treatment, he was expected to attend the center's Family Program—which, he learned was to be part education, part support, and part toolbox for rebuilding. She did not think he would do well with it, writing A: *"Days are long here. At this point, I guess I have to see how he does with the Program. Indeed, I am despairing. There is no question that I must change to get better. Problem I see is that there is a lot for him to swallow when he gets here and while my hopes are high, I am not sure of how he will accept that I cannot go back to the same environment. It's just impossible."* In that same letter, though she continued to refuse to allow him to initiate an insurance claim, she acknowledged the financial toll on the family:

"*I am sick that I am spending money we don't have because I was such a wreck of a person.*" Ever the cheerleader, A responded: "*My sense is that you have got to hang in there. Do not despair. Things are not going to be business as usual when you return. For one, the house operates much differently. There is peace and things are running very smoothly. Everybody (including he) is rooting for you.*"

Throughout his adult life, he was always the transparent type, not one to hide things other than his eating which, as he filled out, was nothing that he could, in any event, hide. In his spirit of inclusion or, one could say, his desire to have company when the days were dark, he forwarded A's email exchanges with her to B and, in doing so, complained that the wreckage seemed to be getting placed at his feet. B had a different take and, in a "*there, I said it*" moment, put in words what everyone else was apparently thinking—the marriage was all over, but the formal dissolution:

First off, I am glad she realizes she must change in order to get better and that she is sick we are spending money because she has been such a wreck of a person. These are good signs. I am hesitant to say she is blaming you for her problems. But she does point to the fact that her relationship with you has been a big factor in her emotional distress. All I can really say about this is that you two have had, since I can remember, a very rocky and unloving marriage. In my opinion you have been separated for at least a decade. I don't think it is either you or her who is at fault since it takes two people to make a successful marriage. I think it will be very good for you, she, and a therapist to talk over things. I doubt that any progress will be made though and I feel that the marriage is long past the time where it could have been saved.

Having said all this, we must again remind ourselves that it has only been 16 days. I imagine things can get better or worse from here depending on her attitude, so we should be sure to see that she embraces the therapy rather than viewing it with a hesitant or conspiratorial attitude.

My final thought for today: I do not like the fact she continues to use A as a pawn between her and you. It is not fair for A. He is in college and should be worried about his own affairs. We already saw what happened when she used A to mediate: She duped him and spiraled out of control. I am even surprised that A is willing to speak to her at the moment.

What a mess. At least the rest of us stand firm in loving solidarity.

He began to prepare for the trip to the center for the Family Program. As the time approached, her counselor called him and outlined what he could expect and what would be expected of him. He was told that the Program was all about the family member or members, not the patient. That resonated well with him, dreading (as he was) having to reprise his enabling husband role in a spin-off, transported to a desert city, of *The She Show*. The counselor also told him that he and she would be allowed to meet on Sunday afternoon following his arrival, but that they were to have no further contact until group sessions on Wednesday and Thursday afternoon, and then lunch together on the last day (Friday). His time and that of the spouses, partners, parents, siblings, friends, and others who had someone in the center was to be spent in lectures, counseling, role playing, and attending Al-Anon meetings. It all sounded fine enough; just the same, he was resistant. He was rather enjoying the continued separation from her, he had plenty of work things going on, and he had no gripping desire or need to see her. He also assumed that she was of like mind. After mulling it over a bit, he managed to adjust his thinking and wrote her of his travel plans, prefacing it with: "*I hope that this time is helping. We are rooting for you and I know you can do it.*"

He left their City house for the airport late in the afternoon. It happened to be Halloween. Though he arrived on time, the flight was delayed and then delayed some more and he spent the time eating and then eating some more. Meanwhile, he was missing an evening with C and D and the enjoyment he always got handing out candy with them and walking around the City house neighborhood with them.

C (with one of the nannies) carried on without him, tending to D. And, C received a call that evening. As C later wrote:

The call came as midnight approached on Halloween of 2010—my first as a high schooler and last as a trick-or-treater. The raspy voice was unmistakable. I had seen all of her movies. And, like many people, I could not escape the 24/7 reporting by the tabloids, in gleeful and schadenfreude fashion, of her troubles.

I am not breaching any confidence or revealing what is not already known. Even the mainstream media reported that, in October 2010, she was at a rehabilitation center. My mother was also there.

Earlier that evening, I helped my 8-year-old brother with his costume. I had also decided to go trick-or-treating. At a certain point, it becomes creepy and somewhat unnatural for teenagers to still be doing that. After all, the spookier and scarier world is that of high school and late adolescence.

That particular Halloween, though, had taken on an inexplicable importance to me—perhaps as a last grasp at what, in reality, was long since gone.

The years leading up to that night were marked by the addictions of my mother, the embarrassment and chaos she caused and the loneliness of needing, but not having her. Painful to watch and even more painful to experience, I had to grow up fast. Finally, as I started ninth grade, my mother left for California and a chance at sobriety.

The phone rang twice before I could get to it, but I already knew who it was by the caller ID.

I was not anxious to talk to my mother just then. It had been a fun evening and probably my last, I knew, going to people's homes and asking for candy. I wanted to savor the moment for as long as possible.

On the third ring, I picked up the phone. The voice said: "Hello, C. This is Lindsay Lohan."

The conversation was brief and, before she passed the phone to my mother, she said: "I just love your mom and I want you to know that she will be home very soon."

That was kind of her. A famous film star telling me that she loved my mother when I found it so difficult to do so.

Wherever one lands on the spectrum from plain bad behavior to a disease, I struggled with how my mother could lose her way and choose alcohol and drugs over family life and healthy pursuits.

Over the remainder of that year, and afterwards, I came to appreciate how good an actress Lindsay Lohan really is. She said what all the other adults had been saying. She knew what I wanted to hear and convinced me, for a time, that there would be a quick ending to all of this. Yet, on that brief call, we both must have known that there would be no quick homecoming.

The hard part was that no one really knew what was going to happen. Addiction is an unpredictable thing. So, too, is the road to recovery. Both are tricky, fraught with relapse, continual disappointment and damage done. Still, I often found myself telling my brother what I could not know (but wished to believe) about our mother's efforts at recovery.

That Halloween, as I put my costume away and took a final bite of candy, I had already begun my transition to adulthood. I knew what I needed to do, and not do. I also realized that no one—not my dad, my siblings, my friends, my teachers, my coaches, my neighbors nor Lindsay Lohan— would be able to help me more than myself.

Arriving at the center on Monday morning, due to the delayed flight, the Program had already started. He registered, which included his relinquishing his cell phone. Never one to show up empty-handed, he had a jeweler friend craft a simple cord bracelet with an oversize bead of amethyst, the gemstone of sobriety, that he planned to give to her when he arrived. He handed the box containing the bracelet to the attendant at the reception area with a request that it be passed along to her. Whether it was or not, he never saw it on her wrist, and she never acknowledged it.

He then joined the 30 or so other participants in a large, sparsely furnished, light-filled interior space. He was asked to introduce himself and, in elevator pitch fashion, explained how he happened to be there. He then accompanied the other family members to a dark, dull auditorium for some get-to-know-you exercises and two lectures. The first speaker told those attending: *"You did not cause it, you cannot control it, and you cannot cure it."* Next was a lecture on substance abuse as a disease.

He wasn't so sure on either point. By then, he had done a Val Kilmer, having morphed from a lean, attractive man to a fat one. At his peak, he was 130 pounds heavier than on his wedding day, with most of the gain in the previous few years. She would, with complete justification, often say: *"What the hell happened?"* Throughout the week, he found himself asking each counselor if his obesity would have caused her alcoholism. He always got the same answer—no. But, make no mistake. If the shoe had been on the other foot and she had ballooned like he had, he would have hooked himself to an IV of Jack to get through it all. He knew that his overeating was symptomatic of his deep disappointment in how he and his life had turned out. The more unhappy and stressed he was, the more he ate and the more he gained. But there was also an utter lack of control, odd for a guy who had been obsessively vain for much of his life. There were things, like shutting his mouth or saying no, that he could have done but did not. Instead, he continued to seek comfort in food, and in his sleek and elegant show dogs which he lavished with affection. He also sought fulfillment in guiding his children, in a non-helicopter-parent way, to successes that he never made for himself or was capable of making for himself.

Turnabout is fair play. If she could not blame him for causing her drinking and drug abuse, then he could not blame her for his lack of control and weight gain.

And he didn't. But she did.

He should have been prepared. As A observed in an email to her: *"Your favorite tactic is to blame others and make their lives a living hell."*

After the morning lectures on the first day, he ran into her as he was walking into the center's cafeteria. They did not embrace, not even an air kiss. Instead, after quickly acknowledging his presence, she stated: *"I want to run this place."* Their talk then turned to the children which, one might think, was reasonably safe terrain. It wasn't, as she quickly tore into him—first about B not regularly reaching out to her. He reminded her that B was out of the country. She did not care. He then snapped back with *"what do you want me to do?"* Not satisfied, she continued to chastise him. He grew increasingly agitated and, each time she paused, he snapped back some more. The interaction did not go unnoticed and, before long, the head of the Family Program appeared and insisted that they go their separate ways. That was an easy cue but he did not take it and lingered instead for more of her grievances and another and sterner reproach from the Family Program head.

He wasn't expecting a vacation and it wasn't, though he enjoyed the camaraderie with his fellow participants, talking travel and philanthropy with the rock star's wife, and the intensity of the sun and the desert heat. The group dynamic and insights shared also made him appreciate that he was not special, and that his experiences of the past few years were happening behind the front door of many homes. On a free evening, he went into the town and walked by and around a famous example of mid-century modern architecture, thinking how wonderful life must be within its confines until he remembered that its original occupant had committed suicide at her other famous home, Fallingwater.

On Wednesday afternoon, the family members were split into smaller groups, each with an assigned counselor. He and the family members in his group followed the assigned counselor to a cramped room filled with a lot of brown furniture and chairs. Two of the chairs had been placed in the center of the room facing each other, about three feet apart. The other chairs encircled them. A designated family member and the individual undergoing treatment had a turn in the two inner chairs. Everyone else was seated in chairs placed around the perimeter. The resident was to speak first, about what had gotten them there. This was to be followed by the family member who was given the opportunity to describe the impact that the drinking or drug abuse had on him or her, and others. The counselor was there to moderate. After the resident and the family member spoke, the counselor then solicited feedback from the group.

He and she would not have their turn until Thursday afternoon. When their names were called, they each got up and made their way to the two chairs and sat down. She started speaking of her "*fondness*" for chardonnay and how it got away from her once she hurt her back and started taking Valium. She spoke of the group sessions that she would lead in her work, as a psychiatrist, and how it some-times felt phony for her to be counseling others on their addictions. She spoke of the need to take better care of her-self. There were no tears, and no palpable remorse. It was all lighthearted, and delivered in a smiling and drunk-lite affect. It was then his turn. He thought *"why am I here?"* and *"where do I go from here?"* A five-minute harangue, calling her out in no uncertain terms, was what he wanted to do and what he thought she needed to hear. He sensed, though, that such an approach juxtaposed against her triv-ializing account would be too aggressive, too jarring, and too incongruent. He decided instead to strike at what really annoyed him about her: her view that the family revolved around her and could not make it without her. In his brief remarks, he described a family that had coalesced and a home life that was operating remarkably well without her. He concluded stating, *"We are fine."* The moderator then asked them to stand and embrace. They stood, but did not embrace. One family member barked out: *"How about a handshake?"* They didn't take the bait, and moved to the open chairs in the circle—choosing chairs that were as far apart as the room would permit. The counselor then opened it up for comments. There were none, other than one from the family member who had urged them to shake hands. This family member asked: *"Is the money really worth it?"*

After the last family member and resident had taken their turn, the counselor then went around the room, person-to-person, asking how he or she felt. When it came to him, he responded: *"I am glad that it is over."* When it came to her, she responded, *"numb."*

The next day, Friday, they were allowed to have lunch together in the center's cafeteria. Later that afternoon, there was to be a ceremony and the distribution of medallions to the family members for having participated in the Program.

The lunch started pleasantly enough, each making

small talk while selecting food from the stations in the cafeteria. Once done, they made their way to an outside patio and sat down. Before he could take two bites of his quesadilla, she had gone from 0 to 60. She began to excoriate him for stating in the Thursday afternoon session that the family was fine, yelling that it was an embarrassing thing for him to say in front of a group of people. She then sneered at his use of "*we*" instead of "*I,*" calling him imperious and pompous. She told him that he came off very, very badly and that the other residents afterwards described him as "*guarded*" and encased in "*armor.*" She screeched that she had been *"pouring out humiliating things"* about herself over the past three weeks and he should have gotten *"naked"* and done the same thing. Repeatedly, she yelled: *"You blew it! You blew it!"* Looking around, searching for help, he caught the eye of the rock star's wife who appeared concerned. A counselor approached, requesting that they keep it down.

He tried to and, in a low voice, began to dissect her vitriol. He told her, first off, that she was the drunk, not he, and that she had incredible nerve berating him. He told her that he did not view the session as one in which the family member was to get "*naked.*" And, he told her that he was not about to apologize for being "*guarded*" and, even if he were that way, so what.

That just inflamed her, and the profanity then spewed

out. Over and over, she told him that she drank as an "*F-you*" to the family. She told him that she drank on the overseas trip that they had taken to visit A as an "*F-you*" to him for having invited C on the trip. She stated that she drank on the family weekend trip as an "*F-you*" to B and C who she claimed had been giving her a hard time. She stated that she drank as an "*F-you*" to the family during the month of September when she was no longer living at the City house. All of this could be heard throughout the patio, resulting in more counselors coming to and circling the table where they were sitting, insisting that they calm down. Neither could at that point. He wanted to tell her to go fuck herself. He did the next best thing. He stood up and said: *"I'm outta here. Congratulations. You are on your own now."*

He called a cab and headed back to his hotel room. While packing his things, he received a call on his cell phone from the center. He hesitated, but then answered it. The head of the Family Program was on the line and, after getting his take on what had happened on the patio, implored him to return to the center for the closing ceremony. He heard her voice in the background matter-of-factly stating to the Family Program head that she had been "*hammering him*" when they were having lunch. After more back and forth, and his weighing the pros and cons, he relented and agreed to return for the ceremony.

He got back to the center about 15 minutes before the ceremony's start. Seeing him, she approached and embraced him. The ceremony was held in the large, light-filled space where the Program had begun. Chairs had been set up in a large circle, with the family members sitting on the chairs and the residents standing behind the chairs. He sat down and she stood behind him. She started to kiss his head and neck, they caressed each other's arms, and he got cringe-worthily emotional.

He flew out, with a layover in another city where he had dinner with a close friend and his friend's fiancé. He was to be the best man at their wedding the following month. He had been a groomsman at his friend's first marriage, now annulled. Listening to him recount the week's event, his friend's fiancé commented that *"she has put you through a lot."* That lingered with him on the flight home, as did the supposed disease aspect to alcoholism.

During this time, a close friend of his from the Lake was diagnosed with breast cancer and was going through chemotherapy, losing all of her hair and being dog sick from the treatment. He received emails from her in which the tone was entirely and remarkably sanguine. To be sure, he thought, those suffering from cancer or any other type of affliction can and do rail against God, the world, and their families. His friend had gotten unlucky. There was nothing that his friend did to have caused the tumors to form. By contrast, to him, the "*F-you*" drinking seemed antagonistic and volitional.

By the time he got back to the City house, a bouquet of flowers had been delivered. There was also an accompanying card with an inscription, but no name: "*I love you more than ever.*" Reading it, he was nonplussed. More than ever, he yearned for the unadulterated truth.

CHAPTER 4

You Keep Me Strong,
I Keep You Strong

The flowers were still fresh yet the bloom was already off the rose. On the day after his return to the City house from the Family Program, C received a call from her. Despite their detachment, spatially and emotionally, the conversation had apparently started cordially enough. Once the pleasantries were out of the way, the conversation—according to C who came to him afterwards, one part tearful and nine parts resentful—shifted course, veering to the confrontational and the accusatory. He was not, even as her drinking and drug use escalated, in the habit of getting in the way of the children's communications with her, or of importuning them for any details. There was hardly a need. Tears, hers or theirs, and his having to mediate or to comfort occurred with some frequency. This time, C was in need of comforting—having been told by her that C was one of the reasons why she drank.

Not too much later, she called him. She was furious, not unlike her mood at the lunch with him two days earlier. While he had trouble, due to the steamed-up manner in which she was talking, absorbing what C had purportedly said to have sparked her ill humor, he did catch her message back which she delivered firmly, loudly, and over and over: *"I will not be told what to do! I will not be told what to do!"* He held his tongue. In the first place, he did not have all of the actual or perceived facts. More fundamentally, he had no interest in an encore of the previous week with her or the likely dressing-down by her should he convey his disgust at what she likely had said to C. Just before she hung up, she told him that she would not be returning to the City house because she did not want to *"live under the same roof"* as C, and didn't want to be around B.

Even if she had not hung up, he would not have talked her out of it. Having had alone time on the return flight to mull over the events of the past few years, he was no longer invested in salvaging a family life that included her.

He was, however, invested in her getting better and in seeing some return on the monetary outlay for the rehabilitation. He also had his own, largely mercenary, and somewhat bourgeois, reasons. If she did not get better, then she could not work, and if she could not work, then he might have to support her for who knew how long. Anticipating the eventual divorce proceedings, the last thing he wanted was to be ordered by a court to pay spousal support or alimony to an unemployed doctor.

Later that evening, as he was sifting through the

incoming bills at the dining room table in the chair oppo-
site to where she would typically perch herself, D sat down
next to him and asked him if they were going to be okay. D
then offered him a fist bump, stating: "*You keep me strong,
I keep you strong.*" That, henceforth, became their salutation and adieu when the going got tough.

He was also coming around to the household senti-
ment that they were looking at a fail. Other than passing his
concerns on to the center's treatment team, he felt out of his
league in orchestrating any kind of positive end result for
her. A was faring no better. A's conversations with her did
not get much beyond who was most at fault and most in
need of changing. In an email recap to her, A wrote:

*I know we had a "heated" conversation the other day. I
think I expressed my annoyance that you continue to call for
"change" at home. The problem is: calling for others to fundamentally change is just not really possible from somebody
in your position.*

*I tried to remind you about the concrete things that
we've done at home. To name a few: (1) Dad—finances,
fiscal responsibility, more involvement (really maximal
involvement because you are absent!); (2) D—much needed
attention and improvement in school; (3) C—therapy; (4) D
and C (and me and B)—overall stability at home; (5) a tidy
home; (6) we are preparing for your return by looking into*

trainers, etc. (certainly, you should also be doing this); (7) there is a great deal of support and communication, love and cohesiveness (and this isn't us versus you). Rather, you would be stepping into this new and vastly improved "environment."

Unfortunately, I don't think you wanted to talk about these things. Instead you brought up his "shopping sprees." Not a smart (or effective) move. If you want to play the game where we trade damaging anecdotes, you lose.

I want to move forward. I want to do the mature thing. I want to focus on and talk about the concrete things everybody is doing to improve themselves and the functioning of the family. I refuse to listen to ancient grievances and I am trying to forget my own. I will try my best to forswear my resentment and memories and encourage others to do the same. And I expect you to figure out whatever it is that is making you so damn angry and forget it. I am convinced that is the only way to move forward.

The time at the center was drawing to a close, and he was not aware of any discussions to extend it beyond that point. They were, thus, rapidly approaching the "*what next?*" stage. He did not recall a module during the Family Program as to what family members can and should expect upon re-entry. The center drummed in the importance of attending Al-Anon meetings but, having sat through a few of them during his time at the Family Program and afterwards, he did not see them as any kind of solution for handling such quotidian matters as getting through breakfast, lunch, and dinner, and everything before, between, and after.

He assumed from the call he had had with her that "*what next*" for her was finding a place to live and, eventually, a mutual and formal end to their sad marriage. Still, nothing had been put in place or much less discussed as, once again, she was communicating with him only through A. Leaving that aside, he was flat out at his job and, too, was in scramble mode on the finances. The October month-end paycheck from one of her employers included only the handful of days that she worked prior to leaving, early that month, for rehabilitation. Not correspondingly reduced in scope was the panoply of month-end bills to pay. Even with his boundless appetite, his plate was full.

A started to play out various scenarios and the strategies for dealing with them, writing him:

So I think the key is not getting bogged down in her nonsense. There needs to be a lot of categorical "NOs," and not indulging her in discussions that give her the opportunity to manipulate us and rehash the past. Firm pushback is key as you've said. C tends to get bogged down of the five of us. She's obviously the biggest liability. B will be mute generally. I think we can expect a lot of hissy fits. Of course, we have to show compassion—that is, willingness to at least try to make this work. This is another area where I fear we will fall short. It is natural to be guarded and not prepared to be warm and fuzzy. But C tends to show a lack of willingness. This would not really be fair. Also, there will be times when legitimate discussion is warranted. We have to be very keen to detect when she has a legitimate need or is being unreasonable. As it turns out, this is easier said than done: we only now realize that we lived under an oppressive regime for two years. Likewise, we can't assume she is being unreasonable and manipulative in every instance.

Even if it doesn't work out with her, I want us to come out of it squeaky clean, knowing that we gave her a fair chance.

For the Thanksgiving weekend, C, D, and he—joined by A—traveled to see his mother/their grandmother at her home. Toward the end of the holiday meal, A received a call from her and went outside to speak with her. After what struck him as a lengthy period, he decided to check on A. Going outside, he noticed that A was still on the phone. Seeing him, A placed the phone on speaker and he could then hear her voice. She kept repeating: *"Your father is so messed up. Your father is so messed up."* He said nothing, and returned to the house.

A few days later, she was discharged from the center. In the early evening, she arrived at the City house with her luggage. He helped her in or, more precisely, he held open the door for her as she got her luggage into the entry hall. He did not stick around and, instead, walked up the main staircase of the house to the former master bedroom where he had moved, the night she left for the treatment center, from a bedroom on the third level (where he had slept alone for some time). A bit later, she made her way to the second level with one of her bags and walked into the room where he was sitting on the bed working. He asked her *"What are your plans?"* She said that she had not made up her mind, other than she had been released to return to work and planned to go back the following week. He told her *"it was nice to hear"* and then informed her that he had taken over the room and she would have to stay in one of the upstairs bedrooms until she found a place to live. Not pleased, she remarked: *"I see you have lawyered up."* He smiled, and that was the extent of the homecoming.

He heard her walk up the back staircase that led to a large hall surrounded by the rooms of A and of B, a family room, and the bedroom that used to be his and that was now to be her temporary quarters. Recalling their wedding vows, traditional fare about for better or for worse and till death do us part, he was not without a measure of conflict and guilt.

The next day, he went to the pharmacy to pick up one of his two prescriptions. On a whim, he asked the pharmacist how he could obtain a copy of his pharmacy records. He was told the store could go back 12 months but that he would have to contact the corporate office for records covering a longer period. He asked for the records available at the store. After paying for his prescriptions, and waiting a few more minutes, the pharmacist handed him a couple of pages of records. He began to walk away, all the while scanning the papers in his hand. He noticed her name, eight times, as the prescribing doctor for a total of 240 pills. He turned and walked back to the counter and asked the pharmacist: *"What is diazepam?"* Told its brand name, he muttered *"Hmm."*

He had never taken Valium. She had never been his doctor.

CHAPTER 5

Burn

As mean as one gets without a gun. Their children never met or laid eyes on her mother who lived within a 20-minute drive of the City house, nor did they ever meet or lay eyes on her father. He, initially, had bonded with her mother who had helped him spruce up the apartment where he lived before the marriage and, over the long period that he and she had dated, he and her mother had socialized on a number of occasions. It was harmonious enough, but it was not to last. The disharmony came at an inopportune time, a few weeks before the wedding. His parents were hosting the rehearsal dinner at a club where he was a member. He had made all of the arrangements including handwriting the invitations on his personal stationery. A neighbor of her mother, who was among the invited guests, received one of the invitations and informed her mother that the writing was illegible. For her mother, it was all about the show. In the "*so-and-so request the pleasure of your company*" part of the wedding invitations, her mother substituted a fictitious middle name for the father's true middle name, believing that the real one sounded too ethnic. The rehearsal dinner invitations, legible or not, fell far short of the exacting standard that went into the wedding invitations.

He learned about her mother's displeasure with the invitations on a day that he and she were at her family's home, visiting her father. Her mother was away on vacation, but happened to call the house when he was there. Learning that he was also at the house, her mother demanded that he be put on the phone. He got up from where he was sitting and went to take the receiver, and said hello. The response was a stern and strident berating about the invitations. Agitated, he started to pace but could not go too far, restricted by the short cord from the wall jack. His plea that *"I thought they were nice"* fell on deaf ears and only inspired her mother to go deeper and take a verbal swipe at his mother, to which he blurted out: *"I resent that."* That enraged her mother even more and, after calling him impertinent, the call ended as did any further communication by her mother with him.

There was a point to be made and likely a legitimate one as, in looking back, the invitations could have been done in a more formal manner and probably should have been handled by his mother and not him. And, in anger, people say things that they might not have otherwise said—though, after some cooling down, there is usually an opportunity to retract or offer some explanatory context to cushion what had been said and allow the relationship to move forward. There was to be no backpedaling with her mother. The consequence of disagreement or any showing of perceived insolence was banishment. Previous fallings out had led to her mother becoming estranged, mostly permanently, from numerous family members.

After that, things got unnecessarily tense. He knew at the time what should have been done and he wanted to call the whole thing off. It would have been inconvenient and messy but they would have all been the better had he actually pulled the plug. The only good that came out of their union—A, B, C, and D—were not in the picture or even imagined at that point in time, and no reason to go ahead.

The rehearsal dinner and then the wedding, a black-tie affair on a Friday evening at the church to which he belonged followed by a reception at the country club to which his parents belonged, did go on. At the rehearsal dinner, her mother did not speak to him let alone acknowledge his presence. The silent treatment continued at the wedding, and her mother did not look at or speak to him except when he was admiring a framed photograph of his parents on their wedding day that her mother had had displayed, alongside wedding photographs of bygone generations, near the wedding cake. Emboldened by the splendor of the evening, his new mother-in-law approached him. There was no softening. Pulling herself up in a confrontational posture, her mother instructed him on the importance of attentiveness to every little detail. He said nothing. Months later, they saw each other again, at a meeting arranged by her father as a possible détente. It went abysmally, ending with her mother telling him that *"these are the rules"* and he telling her mother where she could stick her rules.

For the next 24 years, he never broke bread or the ice with her mother (or her father), nor did they with him—or with her.

She stood by him, perhaps because she felt stuck or perhaps because of the years of callous treatment that she claimed to have received from her mother. She would often describe her mother, a heavy drinker, as insufferably mean. Her father, meanwhile, failed to run interference. Beaten down over the years, her father had become, as put by his father after observing her family's dynamic, a *"castrate."*

In many respects, the apple had not fallen far from the tree. Infused, true enough, with its own distinct pathology, his and her dynamic at the end was much the same.

Much of this was replayed, though with a new twist, in the early days after her discharge from the treatment center when the finger pointing and the laying of blame continued. Her point of view only hardened. She wrote A, copying him: *"The family, as it exists right now IS a problem."* She wrote too that she *"had a tragic childhood and young adulthood and secondary trauma from my jobs, and my mother, and my father."* That was news to him. Though keenly aware that her family had issues, he knew nothing of any tragedy. Nor would he have. Despite five-plus years of dating, they had not had probing conversations where they delved into the recesses of their respective psyches. They did not even undertake a less energetic form of self and other examination. They were young professionals, focused on their careers, and with no depth. Their relationship had drifted and drifted, first into stagnation and then into marriage.

A was sympathetic to a point, writing her: *"I feel for you, believe me, I do. You are not responsible for your Mother's abuse and you are not responsible for the psychological damage that treating sex offenders has perhaps caused. It is tragic that you have become this way. But it is even more tragic that your anger is directed at the family."* She, likewise, had no intention of yielding an inch from her narrative that the problem was the family, not her. She wrote A, copying him: *"So. Here we are. Here I am. I have a husband that was an authentic person at the family program ceremony. That was the single first experience that Dad revealed himself as the same young, handsome, authentic, wonderful, feeling human that he is. That he retreated from this is the single most dreadful loss I have endured."* A dug back in, writing her: *"Did it ever occur to you that you hurt Dad very much and maybe that is the reason he is not warm and fuzzy toward you? Taking out eight prescriptions in somebody's name for diazepam doesn't exactly encourage warmth and fuzziness. What the hell do you expect from a family that lived through your embarrassing and disgusting behavior?"*

A pressed on, and sought to have her detail what she perceived to be the problem with the family:

You say I need some more facts "to make an educated and thoughtful appraisal" of the situation. You then say "The family, as it exists right now IS a problem" but, curiously, do not identify any concrete problems. In my opinion, you're grasping at straws. No family is perfect. Here is what I perceive to be "problems" with our family that you might think are responsible for your unpleasantness:

—Dad's weight

—C's disrespectfulness

Here is one issue that you might have said is responsible for your behavior, but is no longer a valid reason because it has been corrected:

—Dad's lack of involvement in household finances and, as a consequence, frivolousness.

Am I missing anything? I want to reiterate that nobody I've explained the situation to actually believes that these minor family flaws are all that significant. You are on your own with that. If you wish to pursue the line of argument that the family is responsible, you will do so at your peril. It is unproductive and just plain wrong.

Not persuaded, she wrote A and copied him: *"Yes, the family continues to be 'a problem'; I would be happy to flesh this out for you when we get together. The problems are indeed concrete and I only wish the severity of these were trivial."* Still, A asked her to put pen to paper or fingers to keyboard and prepare a memo of sorts to the family about her grievances. Whether she ever did, she never hit send.

He stayed out of the skirmish, preoccupied with his work, with the bills, with the effort to unload the Lake house, with being a source of stability for C, with keeping D strong, with the four dogs, with preparations for the upcoming holiday, and with a trip for the wedding of his friend.

Within days of her return, she started to stay in hotel rooms. Her reasoning was that she could not tolerate C and needed distance. There was, indeed, rancor between her and the exceptionally vocal C that extended well beyond any normal mother-teenage daughter bickering. But there was plenty of space, nearly 5,000 square feet of space, to escape in their City house. By mid-December, after she had spent seven nights in hotel rooms, he was thinking that she had already relapsed or was in a relapse state of mind. Not knowing what to do, he contacted the treatment center for guidance. Little could be done, he was told, other than taking care of himself and the children which he was already doing. The nights spent away in hotel rooms continued and, by the time that he, accompanied by A, left a few days before the Christmas holiday for his friend's wedding, she had spent over one-half of the nights since her discharge in hotels.

Knowing that he could not rely on her to look after things in his absence, nor would he, he arranged to have the two nannies take turns staying all day at the City house during each of the days he would be away. Then, too, B had returned from her quarter abroad and would take charge in the evenings.

The wedding, his friend's second, made him realize that, with luck, it might once again be summertime. After an unhappy first marriage, entered into 33 years earlier, his friend had found the one. At the reception, both the maid of honor and he, as the best man, gave brief remarks. He closed his remarks by stating that *"It is a joyful day and a wonderful life"* and, in a reference to his friend's avocation as a pilot, he ended with *"You fly and now we party."*

The celebration did take off, but neither he nor A partied. Around the time that he was giving the toast, she—

clad in a full-length mink coat and driving her Jaguar—hit another vehicle while traversing a bridge leading from the office building where, through a non-profit corporation, she treated sex offenders. Unbeknownst to him, the evening before, the corporation's board of directors had held a special meeting where they voted to remove her immediately from any service.

He and A learned of the incident from B who had been contacted by the police. An officer informed B that she had an accident, was intoxicated, and had been taken into custody. It later came out from the breathalyzer test that her alcohol content was over three times the legal limit in their state. At the accident site, she failed all of the administered sobriety tests. The criminal complaint noted that *"She was drunk, incoherent and did not know what was going on, or if she was even involved in a crash."* Mercifully, while her car had to be towed, there were no physical injuries.

B gave him the number of the police station where she was being held. He spoke to one of the officers, saying that he was out of the state at the moment and asked for the options, one of which (he learned from the officer) was that she spend the night in jail until he could pick her up the next day. Thinking through the logistics, amidst a lot of anger, he opted for the night in jail. The officer responded *"Are you serious?"* whereupon he got off the phone and contacted a criminal lawyer acquaintance to retrieve her. Meanwhile he and A, while still at the wedding reception, unsuccessfully attempted to get a flight back that evening. They then left the reception and returned to the villa he had rented and called the lawyer. By that point, the lawyer had already picked her up and she was in the back seat of the car. They were told that the police would not allow her to take her personal effects and that she would have to return in the morning for them. A then put the mobile on speaker and they could hear her wailing, loudly: *"I want my fucking stuff! I want my fucking stuff."* The lawyer, to be heard over her wailing, was shouting back at her, telling her that her stuff would be safe and she could get it in the morning. That did not appease her, and they then listened to her wail for another 10 minutes about her stuff, until the car arrived at their City house and she was taken inside.

During this time, he and A had been having conversations with B and C who were apprehensive about being at the house with her. He arranged for one of the nannies to return for the night. He also told B and C that she was to stay on the first level and that they were to call the police if she ascended to one of the upper levels. B and C took knives with them to bed and they and D and the nanny barricaded themselves in the bedrooms on the upper level of the house. The knives did not have to be pulled out, nor did a call have to be made to the police. She remained on the first level throughout the night.

The next morning, while at the airport waiting for his flight, he called her and told her that she needed to go back to rehab and that she should start looking for a place. He had one stipulation: a place with no celebrities or glitz. She agreed, and stated that she and B would start a search. He also learned that a friend of hers would be taking her to the police station so that she could repossess her stuff.

He and A arrived back at the City house in the mid-afternoon, on Christmas Eve. He and she intersected in the kitchen. He looked sharply at her, and said only one thing: *"We are submitting an insurance claim."* She responded, *"Okay."* That aside, he turned his attention to the holiday and to making a happy Christmas for the kids.

By then, he was well practiced at putting on a good face. He also was adroit at making things festive and it was. Before he left for the wedding, he had picked up and, with help from C and D, decorated a blue spruce tree. He had placed cut flowers in vases throughout the first and second levels. He hung wreaths on the iron gates leading into the loggia and from the upper-level windows on the façade of the house, as well as on the detached garage and the portico leading into the kitchen. With some vodka for him and wine for A and B, but not for her, there was a modicum of mirth, all things considered, at least among he and the children.

That was helped by her having the good sense to stay in her room on the upper level of the house and leaving them alone. It was not helped by C insisting that she was "high," an assertion quickly dismissed by him.

There was, however, more wailing. This time it came from D who shrieked: *"He bit me. He bit me."* He dashed from the kitchen to the living room and found D on one of the sofas, with the Doberman nearby, and a mark on D's face.

No one, not even the dogs, was at peace.

CHAPTER 6

Another Casualty

A late-night trip to the vet. For the most part, they were responsible dog owners. They had to be. They had a lot of dogs and, with the exception of the Pug, dogs that looked intimidating. Throughout the neighborhoods of the City house and the Lake house, he walked all four dogs, 360 pounds of dog, at the same time. Everyone had their place, the two boys (the Pug and the Doberman) on the left and the two girls (the Great Danes on the right). The Danes were gentle and dignified, and the Pug was not in a position to do much harm. The fly in the ointment was the Doberman—who was a nipper. Over a nine-year period, the dog had nipped friends of theirs, nipped neighbors of theirs, and nipped workers at their houses. There was never a real bite such that blood was drawn or, but for the night before, a mark was perceptible. He blamed himself, not the breed or the dog. Before acquiring the dog, he had not met the breeder, he had not been around the dog's mother to assess temperament, and he had not picked up the dog at the desirable eight-week point after its birth. Instead, he obtained the dog months later through the person who handled his fawn Great Dane at dog shows. Unfortunately, by then, the dog had spent a lot of time in crates before coming into his hands and their home. Whatever the reason, the dog nipped and it required a great amount of vigilance which, after a few incidents, was largely under control. Looking back, the better course would have been to have found the dog another home. But who wants to take in a known nipper.

On Christmas morning, he got A, B, C, and D (who was not feeling any residual from the run-in with the Doberman) up and they went to church. Upon their return, he started the breakfast and they sat down in the living room on the first level to exchange gifts. The dogs, including the Doberman, perched themselves on their favorite sofas and chairs and took in the action. He had bought all of the gifts and, the evening before, had wrapped them with C's help. It was a far cry from the present orgies that characterized some of their Christmases, but appropriate enough given their changed circumstances. They did not have any particular traditions save writing cards in which they reflected on the year, their feelings for one another, and their wishes for the new year. She descended from the third level, and sat off to herself and remained silent while the gifts were opened.

Throughout the day, C persisted in her running commentary that she was high on something. He did not notice but, then again, he did not take the time to notice. To the extent that they spoke, their conversation centered around the next rehabilitation, her expressed intent to obtain an apartment, and what to do about the Doberman.

In the early evening, he took A, B, C, and D to his club for dinner, something that they had regularly done on holidays. His dinner repertoire did not get much beyond mac and cheese, and he was not about to ask her to cook—nor did she volunteer. He invited her to join them, all the while hoping that she would decline, and she did decline. When they returned from the club, she met them at the door. Then, she got the Doberman and together, with B, they drove to a veterinary facility. He and B sat in the waiting area and she went in with the dog to speak to one of the veterinarians. There was, he thought, a surprising amount of activity on a holiday evening, though he doubted that anyone was there for the same purpose they were. She emerged about thirty minutes later, without the dog who had been put down, and he and she and B returned to the car and began the drive to the City house. Quickly overcome with guilt and a feeling of shame at what might have been a knee-jerk reaction to at least fix something on that Christmas that had gone seriously awry, he lashed out at her—telling her it was all her fault. A heated quarrel ensued. B, in the backseat, repeatedly beseeched them to "*stop fighting.*"

The next morning, he and she and A got into the car and drove to a neighboring county, where her next treatment center was located. No one spoke except for a brief discussion about her future living arrangements. He was relieved to hear her confirm that having her own place was the best for everyone. He pulled into the lot at the facility and parked. Looking around, he was certain that she would need neither a bathing suit nor an autograph book. There was nothing remotely swanky about the frontage or the environs. They walked to the entrance and, once in the vestibule, she turned and said that she did not want them to go in. They assented, and said their goodbyes. She hugged A. She and he did not hug, but he wished her well. He and A got back into the car and lingered for a few minutes, thinking that she might turn around and walk out. She did not, and he and A then departed. The truth is that they could not get away any faster.

A few days later, he and A went back to the facility to attend a program for families and friends of the residents. Afterwards, they went looking for her and found her in a corridor near her room on the main floor. She was sitting on a bench and they stood looking down at her. She then, for some unknown reason, showed them a paper she had been clutching. It was an intake sheet of sorts which she handed to A who, after examining it, pointed to an entry that indicated that she had last had Valium on December

24 and 25. A questioned her about it. She responded that it was a typo. He took the paper from A's hand and then drilled in, asking how it could be a typo and why it was even there. Not having a reasonable explanation, she finally admitted that she had taken Valium while at the house after the DUI. A blurted out: *"You just lied to us."*

C was right again . . . only 15, but with acute drugdar.

CHAPTER 7

Round Two

A hot mess. There was to be no out-of-sight, out-of-mind on the second round of rehab. She wasn't, to begin, multiple states away, and there were fewer restrictions on who she could call and when, though she had to make the calls on a communal pay phone used by all the residents, and had to contend with the other residents who were using the phone when she wanted to use it or who wanted to use the phone when she was using it. This time, the calls went to him and not A. And, she called him daily, sometimes twice or three times daily, giving him the blow-by-blow or at least what he could make out from the background chatter of those waiting to make a call.

He also received calls from her assigned counselor who contacted him on multiple occasions. He went through the same drill as on the first round, being asked many of the same questions and giving what was becoming his canned responses to them.

From the start of what was to be a three-week stint, he sensed that the fit was not a good one. He also sensed that she was determined to control the process and do it on her terms, rather than let the process unfold and possibly get to a better place. She also had specific ideas as to what that place would be as, within a short time, she told him that she wanted unfettered access to the City house. He reminded her that she had agreed that she would look for living arrangements of her own. That did not matter to her, it being her view now that an essential element of her path to recovery was the ability to come and go to and from the house and their lives. After a disquieting few weeks following her discharge from round one, including her having spent 12 of the 23 nights, between the time of her discharge from the last rehabilitation center and her drunk driving arrest, away from the City house, he had no interest in that kind of access. In an effort to get her to appreciate how strongly he felt on the subject, he bypassed her and went to her counselor, hoping that the counselor would impress upon her the intensity of his feelings on the subject. He wrote: *"We are united in our view that she cannot return to the house. If she does attempt to do so, I—with the kids' full support—will instruct my divorce lawyers to proceed with the filing of divorce papers. The papers will include a petition for exclusive possession of the residence. Another option is for me to move out of the house with the kids and the dogs. Under either scenario, she will not be living with us."*

The kids would also have none of it. A wrote her:

I was a little surprised by what I heard from Dad. Apparently, you don't want to live in an apartment? You suggested that you live at home? If any of this is this the case, it seems you are reneging on what you said you would do and on what you agreed was appropriate when we dropped you off at rehab.

Until you get your life back together and are religious about your various therapies, you are not welcome at home. C and D have suffered a great deal and I will not allow you to disrupt their lives anymore. I will relentlessly defend them from your illness.

I'm sorry to say that you have turned me into a cold-hearted cynic now that I have gone in circles with you for many months. We are not conspiring against you. We simply want peace and quiet and love and structure in our lives.

B wrote her: *"You cannot come back into the household, bringing chaos as you did before. My deepest concerns are for the well-being of C and D, and I will do anything to prevent their lives from being ruined."*

C wrote her: *"At this point, I feel more determined than ever to make sure that you stay away from MY family and me until you choose to be sober. If you choose to keep drinking and pill popping, then you are not welcome in MY house."* C also wrote:

Your so-called abusive mother did not cause this. Your family did not cause this. Your "insolent" teenager did not cause this. Your work did not cause this. You caused this.

I am the one with the abusive mother. You have beaten me down with your endless drinking, pill popping, and cold heartedness.

I truly thought that maybe you would come back from rehab with wholehearted appreciation for what you have put me through. Instead, on December 23, 2010, you chose to get a DUI and ruin my Christmas. It will go down as just another one of the holidays that you have fucked up.

This is a time in a girl's life when she needs her mother most. She needs her mother to help her pick out the right outfit for a dance. She needs her to help her with her homework. She needs her to comfort her after a fight with a friend and be there when she is having a lousy day.

I'm not that girl and you are not that mother. Instead, you get wasted and high.

She must have gotten the message as, soon thereafter, she called him and said: *"You won."* Just to be sure, he had the locks changed on the City house.

He then went apartment hunting and, in doing so, returned to what he knew—the pre-war building where they had lived prior to moving to the City house. One of the penthouses was available and he snapped it up.

At the end, there was to be no graduation ceremony from this rehab nor a quick move into the apartment. In one of her frequent calls, she advised him that "*on the table*" was her being referred to another treatment facility. She told him that she was "*too big a fish*" or something along those lines and that the current center's "*pond*" could not accommodate her. The treatment center being considered for her, he was told, had a patient demographic consisting largely of healthcare professionals with addiction and professional licensing issues. She now had both.

While she was resistant to more rehab and to a transfer to another center, he was more accepting of the turn of events, despite a projected cost of over $40,000. In one of their calls, when she was up in arms about the likely direction, he asked her to step outside of herself and give her assessment of the situation—assuming that the transfer was being recommended for someone else. She told him that she would agree. He said: "*Then you need more help.*" In that call, she stated to him, "*You must just want to shoot me now.*" He did not have a gun and, in any event, did not let on. He simply stated, "*I just want you to get better.*"

Nothing had been easy or seamless, and that was not going to change. The new treatment center was in a different state and she would fly to it. There was another complication. She would be discharged by the current treatment center on a Friday and then would leave for the new center the following Monday. In the intervening weekend, she would return to the City house on the condition that he commit to being responsible for monitoring her over the entire weekend and ensuring that she made it to the next facility. Against his better judgment, but not having a reasonable alternative with A and B back in college, he agreed.

He had one of the nannies pick her up at the rehab facility. He also arranged to have both nannies alternate hours over the weekend such that one of them was at the City house at all times except at night.

He was at the house when she arrived. On entering, possibly because she knew him too well, she went to the door leading from the kitchen to the portico and the backyard, set the lock, and then inserted her key. The key would not open the lock. He watched, quietly, as she tried it over and over. Figuring out what had been done, she let out a loud cry. She then grabbed the landline phone in the kitchen and went to the lower level where she called her now former business partner and he could hear her convulsing for what seemed like an interminable period.

Having exhausted herself, she went to the bedroom on the third level where she remained for the rest of the evening. They did not speak that evening and barely spoke the entire weekend. There was really nothing to say. The nannies, rotating throughout the weekend, ran interference. At night, feeling uneasy with her presence in the house, his sleep was fitful.

By Sunday morning, with the reality that he was expected to write a big check as the first installment for what was to be round three, he began to draw back. He also wanted something in return. He wrote out an "Agreement" that was intended to capture in watered-down fashion, because he knew that anything remotely legalistic would not fly, their reciprocal commitments. This was all wishful thinking as she was more lucid than he imagined. She read through it, again and again, picking it apart. The best that he could work out with her was her agreement to cooperate on the bills and the sale of the Lake house. Having come to terms with giving up the Lake house, he wanted to be done with it. But, since they were both owners, he had to get her written authorization to adjust the sale price. He made the changes. Once printed, she reviewed it and they signed it.

Witnessing his unsuccessful attempt to persuade her to enter into a more expansive agreement, C sent him an email later in the day:

I realize that you are doing your best right now. Mother's reaction to the separation agreement could not have been predicted. There are three issues that I have with what went on today. I thought that it would be better to write an email rather than complain to your face.

Mother's personality, attitude, and overall person will never change. She may be able to get over the drugs and alcohol but it will always be about her. You need to let her know that she can act like this on her own time. I will not put up with her utter nonsense.

Whether or not we like it, she will have to go back to rehab. Not just because of her license, but because she needs to at least attempt to get healthy. I don't like to watch you be thrown around by one person. I have watched you be manipulated, duped, pushed around, and beaten down for over three years. It is about time that you show her that you aren't going to spend the rest of your life picking up the pieces for her. Whether it is dishes, laundry, or a DUI, you are always cleaning up her messes. You always say that we should take care of ourselves first.

Please consider making the next step in the process. That means getting the apartment together. I am willing to help you with this because I feel that it is in my best interest and D's as well. This weekend has been completely unhealthy for all of our mental, physical, and emotional states. Taking the next step also involves doing anything you need to do to take care of yourself. I do not want to push you into doing the legal things that may be necessary. All I know is that money

won't buy you love and it certainly won't buy you happiness.
I'm not going to play around anymore. If you want to then
be my guest. My childhood has been completely cut short.
D's is being ruined. You need to do something to break her
line of destruction.

He took her to the airport early on Monday morning. This time, they arrived well in advance of boarding and, after checking her bags, he accompanied her to security and waited. She did not say goodbye and did not turn to wave or acknowledge his continuing presence as she passed through.

He lingered and watched her remove her coat and effects to go through the scanner. He noticed that she was wearing a white dress shirt. It was way too small for her, quite tight really. He could also observe her belly protruding from it and overflowing onto her jeans. She had, now that he looked, put on a lot of pounds. Having been the target of her fat-shaming, he allowed himself a sardonic smile.

CHAPTER 8

A Beautiful Day

He was giddy. He strode out of the airport terminal and made his way to the underground short-term parking lot and to his vehicle, a white, blinged-out Lincoln Navigator. It was his fourth Navigator. Each one, as the model evolved, was more ostentatious or, depending on one's perspective, more vulgar than the next. When he saw it for the first time and took in its massive grill, he was gleeful. To be sure, it had a utilitarian purpose. A Prius would likely not have accommodated his dogs, or his sense of luxe, in the trips to and from the City house and the Lake house. It would, as it turned out, be his last Navigator. Enough time had passed since she, at his insistence, had moved out for him to have fully appreciated that his big life was all over, but for the sell-off. Still, changing the fundamentals takes time, and it was certainly not going to happen that morning. Clicking the key fob and opening the door, the running boards descended. Jumping over them, he hauled his bulky frame into the driver's seat. If he thought that the large vehicle was slimming, he was mistaken. He was, though, considerably lighter that morning, having provided her with a big fat check to cover the initial expenses on her next rehab.

It was not even 8 am and the morning was already a magnificent one, like the morning of the party at the Lake house. The sky was a rich blue, and cloudless. The temperature was very crisp, but not freezing. Had the sky not been so blue, it might have felt colder. For him, having just surfaced from a hellish, anxiety-ridden weekend where he felt uneasy and fearful of triggering another outburst such as what occurred when she discovered that he had changed the locks to the City house, any air, no matter how biting, was welcome. C was right, once again. The weekend had been an unhealthy one for all in the house who had to endure it, including for her—being between treatment facilities and in forced confinement with an estranged husband who had no words for her, nor she for him.

Buckling himself in and then pressing the start button, he pulled out of the parking spot and headed toward the airport exit. He inserted his credit card at the pay station, and off he went. Once he got on the highway, he pumped the accelerator and turned the CD on and up. Out came blaring: *"It's a beautiful day. Don't let it get away. It's a beautiful day."*

He was blissful and, despite his excesses and heretofore free-lunch mentality for which he had already begun to pay dearly, it was hard not to cut him some slack and allow him a bit of merriment. For the first time in a very long time, he was hopeful: *"Teach me. Take me to that other place. I know I'm not a hopeless case."* And for the first time in a very long time, he had a plan: *"It was a beautiful day. Don't let it get away."*

It being a federal holiday, there was not the heavy Monday morning traffic and so the drive to the City house from the airport went more quickly than usual. In any case, he was in no hurry. Flipping the CDs, and wrapped in the security of his capacious drive, he took in the scenery along the route that he had traveled many times in the past and thought of the path forward. Later that morning, he would email his brother-in-law, writing: *"She's gone!!! We had the first day of the revolution as A famously proclaimed in late August. Today is the first day of the rest of my life."*

But, where does a guy in his mid-50s start? And was she really gone? At the moment that he turned into the driveway of the City house, his cell started to ring. She was calling. Hesitating briefly, he tapped accept and said hello. She was in the process of boarding the plane and simply stated: *"Thank you."* He responded, telling her that there was no need for that, he thought she was courageous, and he was optimistic it would go well. Whether he believed it or not mattered little. The day was about hope, and self-betterment. She called him later that morning to let him know that the plane had landed and she was being transported to the treatment facility. Unlike her condition when she arrived at the first treatment center, he could tell that she was sober. There was no need to call C for any validation. This was now serious, not drunk-lite or "save for my scrapbook," stuff.

After the short call with her, he made his way into the house and was greeted by the two Great Danes and the Pug. He leashed each of them and they walked the neighborhood, the beloved Danes going to his right and the Pug going to his left. The Doberman would have gone to his left, but the deed was done and he did not give much thought to the dog or its demise, at their hands, that morning.

Checking on C and D, he told them he planned to be at his office for a few hours, and then was going to work out with his trainer, after which he would take them to a museum exhibit. He and D fist-bumped, each stating that he would keep the other strong. On his way to work, he stopped at the leasing office for the apartment he had secured for her, paying the security deposit and the first month's rent. He planned to get it furnished and have it ready for her return, which he anticipated would be in six weeks. Little did he know then, but it would be a long time before she would be discharged from the treatment center and take up residence in the apartment. That mis-calculation meant month after month in rent for a vacant apartment, along with month after month of checks to the treatment center.

He then made his way to his office and began to tackle his to-do list. By then, the hypnotic exhilaration of the drive from the airport had worn off. A colleague with whom he was working on a matter came into his office and asked him how he was doing. Inexplicably, as he was not the type to wear his emotions on his sleeve nor was he one to share the domestic unrest even with those in whom he occasionally confided, he responded by bursting into tears. He quickly pulled himself together, muttering that he was fine—appearances notwithstanding. He was actually far from fine, but it was not the time to go soft. He hadn't up to that point, and he wouldn't going forward.

It was a beautiful day. He wasn't going to let it get away. He wasn't a hopeless case.

CHAPTER 9

Purgatory

When do we get out? The upgrade in treatment facilities came with a corresponding upgrade in diagnoses. Shortly after she was admitted to the third facility, her assigned counselor contacted him to go over what, to him, were now the basics and, during the conversation, described her as being *"very sick."* That, from his vantage point, was simply a politer way of saying that she is a *"hot mess."* Whichever it was, he was by this time becoming far less interested in her well-being and much more interested in his own equanimity and that of their children.

His and theirs would have to wait, though. He first had to get through another tiresome round of questions as to what had gotten them to this point. Were that not enough, and unlike the first center which restricted contact with family members even during its family program, this center encouraged contact and scheduled calls during which he and she, along with the assigned counselor, would talk. The first session went well enough, mostly an exchange of niceties and how she was settling in. Shortly into the second session, the gloves came off and degenerated into accusations by her that he was turning the children against her. The counselor was not effective, nor was it realistic to expect otherwise, in mediating matters between two people who, with years of history, had had enough of each other and knew just what buttons to push. Minutes after the call ended, and stoked by his fury over her recriminations, he shot off an email to the counselor, writing:

I am not the alcoholic and the drug abuser, and I have not caused my kids harm as she has done. Thus, to suggest that I am wielding some power over the kids or that I have the ability or desire to drive a wedge between them and her is utter nonsense. We have lived through her alcoholism and drug abuse for years now. We have lived through her autocratic, her-way-or-the-highway personality for years. I am not subjecting myself to it any longer. That she cannot think of anyone but herself and that she has no appreciation of what I have done for years, and am doing now, to hold the family together is pathetic. I don't think that I heard a simple "thanks" on the phone today. That she is insisting on warm and fuzzy now after spending 12 of 23 nights in hotel rooms in December binge drinking, after being 3x over the legal limit when she was arrested on December 23, and after being high on Valium in our home on Christmas eve and Christmas day shows just how clueless she is about the feelings and emotions of the rest of the family. Had anyone been listening today, my message is that the ball is in her court to show that she can comply and get into a sustained recovery. Unfortunately, she wants everything on her terms and on her time frame.

He shared the email with A, B, and C in what he expected would be some continuing dialogue with them about where this was all heading and where it might likely end up. B jumped in, writing: *"This is very bad, indeed, that the counselor thinks you are 'manipulating' us against her. Nonsense. I am sick and tired of this bullshit."* A replied: *"Bullshit, I am able to think for myself. Very offensive. Tell that to the counselor. That's all I have to say."* C didn't enter the fray, focused as she was in making the best of her high school years.

Later that evening, he reflected back on their ugly spat at the first center. He was determined not to wade into those waters again, and sent the counselor another email:

You should also know that she acted exactly as she did today with me as she did when I attended the family program at the other center. She was trying to punish me. That is not going to happen on this go-around and, so, we may need to rethink any further calls until such time that she can act in a civil and courteous manner.

Rather than being confrontational and threatening,

she should be grateful that the family is willing to do three sequential rehabs. With this, we will be nearly $80,000 into rehabilitation costs. This is money that we do not have. And, I can confidently state that she would not pay one dime for me to be in rehab were the shoe on the other foot. But I am not her and am doing this for her and for the kids so that she might have some relationship with them down the road should she choose to abstain from alcohol and drugs.

They all then took a break for a few weeks.

As the rehab entered its fourth week, the counselor resurfaced and, in an email to him, expressed that the *"reactivity"* in the family is *"highly escalated"* and that a *"contributor to the degree of escalation"* was his *"anger"* with her. That counselor then asked him to respond to a series of questions, including: (i) *"Is the marriage in fact over?"*; (ii) *"Is the long-term goal some form of repair of the relationship with the children?"*; (iii) *"Do you think she will be able to gain self-control in sessions with you?"*; and (iv) *"What is your goal?"* Reading and rereading the commentary and questions, he surmised that the counselor, rather than at least feigning impartiality, had concluded that he was no day at the beach.

Maybe he was a walking disaster, and an angry one at that. All the same, the counselor had little clue as to what was going on in his life let alone, and more importantly, the lives of A, B, C, and D—who were not cloistered in the protectiveness of the center.

Sharing the counselor's questions with A and B, and letting them know that he considered the questions to be intrusive, B tried to alter his thinking, writing him: *"I don't think that the Q and A is intrusive at all. They should know this information in order to proceed with treatment. She should also know this information so she doesn't have unrealistic expectations when she gets out."* A opted to take a swing at answering them for him: *"In my view, the first question is quite fair. In fact, the marriage is in separation and, functionally, cannot be rightly called a 'marriage.' The answer to the second question is yes, hopefully, but it's not in your control, you're not willing to put in much effort on this and, fundamentally, it is up to the kids. The answer to the third is: not likely. No confidence that she will have self-control in the near future. The answer to the fourth, presumably, is that you're done with her."*

There was, A was correct, no marriage, and even if the children were receptive to it, he was way out of his depth in brokering a rapprochement between her and them. He was, in any event, not up to the challenge—drained from being blamed for something that the first center told him he didn't cause, can't control, and can't cure. But, he was not about to yell *I want a divorce!* in a crowded rehab center. Instead, he ended up giving a bunch of circumspect non-answers which, since he was not contacted again, must have been all that was needed.

As the rehab entered its eighth week, he had the option of going to its in-person family program. He begged off attending, not seeing any point in a reprise of the first center's family program and the potential for further verbal lacerations. But he did have occasion to see her for a short time while on a business trip to the city where the center was located. He was not, by a long shot, looking forward to seeing her, but the strangeness of being in the same city without at least a quick drop-by left him uneasy. And, there was a pressing need for that drop-by: the Lake house was still on the market, and was overpriced for the market, but the realtors would not allow him to reduce the price without her express written consent on their form. They then arranged to meet at the center.

Upon arrival, he signed in and the receptionist called for her. When she approached the reception area, they did not bother to pretend any pleasure at seeing each other and, instead, they greeted each other in a dry, emotionless, and halting manner. She took him on a tour, and he met her counselor. After that, and with the realtor paperwork in hand, he explained that the price on the Lake house had to be reduced. He started gently, with some mild cajoling, reminding her of her written agreement, entered the day before the start of the third stint at rehab, to cooperate in its sale. Then, seeing that he was getting nowhere, he switched to a more portentous approach, describing a scenario, if she would not agree, of his immediately stopping payments on the mortgage and the home equity loan, and letting the house go into foreclosure. She balked but, as he was about to get into the taxi to go to his business meeting, she signed the papers and thrust them in his hand. He was relieved—less about the thought of the house that he loved slipping away into foreclosure and more about his getting away from her.

To him, the brief time together brought to mind the eternity of forced coexistence that faced the souls damned in Sartre's *No Exit* for their earthly misdeeds. Hell is each other, he and she likely thought.

Back to the City house after the quick trip, and vowing, at least in this life, that he would not again be confined alone in a space with her, he and one of their nannies got to work and made the penthouse apartment that he had secured for her walk-in livable. They equipped the place from stem to stern—from the art to the bathroom soap. As they surveyed their work, he expressed that, absent the two oversize portraits of her which were placed in her new bedroom, he would have been perfectly happy to take up residence in the place.

As the rehab entered its 12th week, the government surfaced. First, he received a call at his office from a Drug Enforcement Agency representative. Listening for a moment to a half-dozen pointed questions about drug prescriptions being written in his name, he quickly deflected the inquisitor to where the probe should rightly be focused—her, and he declined to say anything else.

Next, despite her espoused superiority to him on money matters due to the very long ago check he had bounced, she had not kept up on the necessary quarterly tax filings over the year. The tax liability, in the hundreds of thousands of dollars, started his big liquidation. He cashed out an account he had with his employer, withdrew the cash-surrender value on a whole life insurance policy, raided his 401(k) plan, and drew on a joint line of credit. He had no choice.

Though his excessive spending was all but reformed, the timing of his epiphany on pecuniary matters was unfortunate. He was not able to do much about it. The reimbursement from his employer's health plan for the out-of-pocket rehabilitation charges had not come through; there had been no offers on the Lake house; their home life, including the four tuitions, along with salaries for two nannies and one housekeeper, was cripplingly costly; and cash continued to flow out to pay for more and more rehab.

As the rehab entered its 16th week, she started to assert her conditions for re-entry. Among them was her insistence that she be given a key to the City house, it being her intention to come and go as she pleased. She also claimed that she had the center's support and, without access to the City house, her stay in the center would just be prolonged. That prompted him to complain to personnel at the center who, in response, assured him it was not the center's view that she be provided a key to the City house. He was further told that, if her stay were to be extended, it had to do with her being behind on the "*time line*" and her continuing to blame him for her plight. That was good to hear, as tendering a key to her was, for him, a non-negotiable proposition.

After the call, he wrote B: *"This is so messed up and such a colossal waste of my time and everyone else's."* B responded: *"I don't know why, after nearly six months in rehab, she is not taking responsibility for her actions and current situation. We just have to plan for a safe future for the rest of us. I strongly think you should get a legal document/court ruling saying that she cannot come to the house of her own will. I have been having these thoughts that she will show up to the house drunk, angry, and hysterical, another reason she shouldn't have a key and that we should get a court ruling."*

The *coup de grace* or what finally threw him over the edge, was her subsequent insistence that he would have to pay another $10,000 in continuing rehab charges. Stuck for too long in purgatory, he was weary of the tithes and wanted an exit. He refused to make another payment.

In June 2021, as the rehab entered its 19th and final week, on top of the six weeks at the first center and the two weeks at the second center, and entirely unrelated to his decision to stop paying for any more rehab costs, she was conditionally discharged and started life in her new apartment. Her discharge brought no boost to their financial state. Though out of the center, she was not permitted to return to her former life of working—constrained, at least temporarily, by a licensing predicament. It would not be for another 15 months that she would work again. Happily, during this time, she was diligent in avoiding alcohol.

At some point that fall, she wrote him stating: "*I am grieving terribly my loss of you, and that is the single worst aspect of my recovery.*" Words back to her escaped him. Not for one instant did he believe she was grieving about him, nor for one instant did he believe he was grief-worthy.

CHAPTER 10

A Recovery of Sorts

Exit. What kept him up at night with thoughts of destitution eventually came to a head. It started with a Thanksgiving dinner at his club. In spite of the passage of nearly six months since her discharge from the third rehabilitation center, he could see that relations between her and A, B, and C remained strained and largely non-existent. In an effort to inject some warmth, he invited her to join them all for the holiday meal. They had an agreeable enough time, with him steering the conversation to the food and other light fare. That was followed with a note from her in which, after thanking him for including her, she wrote: *"I know fully well the financial morass at present; I give you my assurance that I would never make unnecessary additional strain."* Meanwhile, she had obtained legal counsel and what also followed was his being served with a complaint, filed with the local family court, for spousal support payments.

There was a certain irony to it. Having made the decision, month after month, to write Valium prescriptions for herself in his name, she now sought to have him bear the fallout from those decisions—the suspension of her medical license and her corresponding inability to work. He did not have much energy to dwell on the ridiculousness of the situation. For him, as every incoming cent was needed and with nothing to spare, his time was better spent engineering ways that Peter would pay Paul.

Unlike in a divorce action, the laws in their state allowed the respondent in a spousal support action to interpose marital misconduct as a defense. After talking himself off the ledge, he called her and let her know that he would have his lawyers fight hard to defeat her claim—all the while knowing that his stance would force her, if her desire for support from him was earnest, to file a complaint for divorce against him. She went that route, later gloating to him that A and B *"expressed relief that the filing was finally done and their overwhelming support of divorce has been the precious small gift of comfort I have found in a long time."* She also wrote: *"You probably need to know."*

While he was soon encumbered with direct payments to her in the months leading up to the divorce, ultimately it had little impact. It was just more money, and debt. Instead, after figuring a way to keep afloat, he then focused on more profound distress—at least as he felt it. He had been grieving the loss of his black Great Dane, at the age of 11, and would soon be grieving the loss of his fawn Great Dane, also at the age of 11. Both passages precipitated endless crying jags in his office and elsewhere. He loved them, and they he. He did not golf, and his tennis and waterskiing days had passed him by. In place of that, he derived much happiness in being with the Danes, whether on long walks on the beach at their Lake house or runs throughout their City house neighborhood. Fortunate for him, his Pug stepped up and pulled him through it, saving his life. In time, the intense sadness of the two losses started to ease.

None of the awful financial things he played out in his mind came to fruition. The Lake house did not go into foreclosure, and it was sold. As it turned out, he was pretty good with finances. All bills were paid on time and, eventually, the debt started to whittle away. Throughout, with razor-sharp intensity, he tackled one credit card balance or indebtedness at a time, paying it off, and then moving to the next one. At the same time, he whacked away at the expenses and, whether small like a cable bill at the Lake house or big like his Navigator, he got rid of them. He had learned, adopting a cash-and-carry approach to money, save for a smallish mortgage, years later, on a smallish cottage at the lake. His addictive spending was rehabilitated, and he would not relapse.

After a short while, she got her divorce. Not surprisingly, there was little to fight over. He walked away with his watches and his many architect-inspired eyeglasses and his Pug. She walked away with her furs and her jewelry and her handbags and her Jaguar. They had the art which, during the divorce negotiations, they spent two tedious sessions going one by one, he first, then she, then he, selecting pieces. Blissfully for him, shortly before she got her divorce, she was given permission to work again, and his payments to her came to an abrupt and final end.

There was still more, as far as he was concerned. The day after the court entered the divorce decree, he instructed his lawyers to file a petition against her for the support of C and D who had been living full-time with him and who would continue to do so until their respective college matriculations. He also that day filed a petition with the Tribunal of the local Roman Catholic Diocese, seeking an ecclesiastical annulment of the marriage. He wanted to leave open the door for marrying in the Church, something not permitted of divorced Catholics; and he wanted more than a civil dissolution. He wanted a different outcome—treatment of the marriage as if it had never existed.

He obtained the support, which she had to pay for nearly eight years and, a few years after he filed for it, he obtained the annulment. The Tribunal wrote him: *"Your marriage was invalid under the law of the Catholic Church."*

• • •

What mattered? All along, it was the children.

D, once finding a voice, turned out to be the detached and *laissez-faire* one of the pack. More interested in the whys and the wherefores, D asked why two people well into their 40s and already having three children would have a fourth child or the reason, after she had gone down one career path, they would underwrite a lengthy and expensive second career path for her. D also began to charter an independent and singular track. Resistant, in many ways to his proneness to micromanage, D would say to him: *"I don't want to be one of your show dogs."*

C, by contrast, was not detached and bluntly expressed the difficulties that were likely felt, to some extent, all around, writing him: *"We have both lived through much of the same traumas in life. Experienced through different eyes, yes, but the same. Devastating alcoholism, the loss of a wife and mother figure, dissolution of a marriage and family, difficulty accepting change, failure to meet personal goals. We've experienced these things together."* C continued: *"It has been a terrible road for the both of us. I had a hard and unfortunate childhood. I now have trouble sleeping, have terrible anxiety. I am hotheaded, intense, hasty with my words and aggressive at times. Over time, I will work through these issues. I would take a wild guess and say that you, too, have many of these same issues as a result of what you have gone through and that you, too, will work through these."*

A and B were more stoic and, affirming his earlier prediction that they would learn from their parents' mistakes and would lead more fulfilling lives, they each made quiet and meaningful changes to their vision of a life well lived. A wrote of the need *"to focus on things that really matter in our short, unpredictable lives."* A also wrote: *"If none of this had happened, I'd be setting myself on the same path as my parents, pursuing money, things, and prestige at the cost of my true passions. But now, having seen how that story plays out, I have chosen a different path."* B wrote: *"It was difficult to comprehend how someone so intelligent and successful on paper could be failing in life. It was also disheartening that a key female figure, the model of my idea of success, could no longer serve as an example to me. This learning process led me to realize key components missing from my model of success: the need for balance; the importance of healthy choices; the virtue of patience through life's inevitable setbacks and difficulties."*

Eventually, pendulums swing back and it happened to her. This did not occur because she went about making "amends"; she certainly had not with him and, even if she had with the children, words would not have moved them. They wanted a turnabout and, early on, had outlined just what that would be. A had written: *"Until you get your life back together and are religious about your various therapies, you are not welcome at home."* Then B had written: *"You cannot come back into the household, bringing chaos as you did before."* Thereafter C had written: *"If you choose to keep drinking and pill popping, then you are not welcome in my home."* The quid pro quo for her re-entry was heard by her loud and clear. Rather than defiance, it was taken to heart. And so, a new normalcy would form. In time, the disharmony in her relations with the children gave way to peace, their distrust gave way to affection, and their anger and resentment gave way to a measured admiration. The revolution was over.

There was to be a relapse, he becoming aware of it after she texted him early one Saturday morning to retrieve her from an emergency room where she had been taken to detoxify. Walking to her car, she asked him to open the back door and pointed to a large bag out of which he pulled a jeroboam of vodka, with little more than a shot glass left. He told her that she would have to stay at his house until she could sort out the next steps. On arriving, she was met at the door by D who remarked: *"This is the most irresponsible thing that you have done."* She did have to return to another rehabilitation center, but there would be none of the turbulence associated with the other centers. Quickly after intake, she was discharged and has not relapsed again.

She had gone through a very rough patch, taking them all down with her. But rather than let it forever define her and her relations with the children, she worked long, hard, and successfully to lead a temperate life. That is what the children wanted, and that was her redemption.

For him, as C had foretold, he had much to work through. First up was a relatively quick and easy 60-pound weight loss. Equally quick and easy was his ability to put it back on, take it off again, and so on. He failed to heed the entreaties, direct and indirect, from his doctors and from the children. Trying to get him on track after exasperating yo-yo losses and gains, A wrote him:

I want this year to be a year of health—mental, physical, spiritual. In my mind, this has to be the foundation for living a good life. I've found there are so many paradoxes and tradeoffs in life. For example—I'll just binge on all this food because it'll make me feel better in the moment, but in the long run it destroys willpower, health, self-esteem, body image—in short, everything you need to live a good life. I see a lot of you in me—makes sense after all since you made me. I think that you work too much, I think that you worry about compensation too much, I think that you worry about what others think too much. All things I see in myself. I'm disturbed by some of the dark things you say about the future, like how long you'll live or how miserable your future is thanks to your finances. Let's work together to improve ourselves.

He never abandoned the work on his weight issues, but he was never successful for any enduring period. Inexplicably, he allowed a lack of control to shape and ruin his life. Apart from that, and though he sunk at times into dark periods and angst about the future, his was not a bleak house, and he knew it. Luckily, the fog that had enveloped him had continued to lift and he came to the realization that his adulthood search for more was misguided. He already had everything that he might want or need. He also had weathered the storm and, mattering the most, he had held it together for the kids. That was his redemption.

One had to wonder whether it all had to happen or, if it did, whether it had to be as hard as it was. Maybe, it was simply the natural progression and expected outcome for two mismatched people, both too naïve and unaware when they ostensibly committed to each other years earlier. Maybe, instead, it was just the natural progression and expected outcome for two people who had loved each other but got caught up in themselves, in their careers, and in their stuff. They stopped paying attention, and they stopped making an effort. There is no redemption for that.

EPILOGUE

December 2013. The pending sale of the City house, over a year after it was listed, was cause for much jubilation. The proceeds would wipe out any and all remaining debt, unfettering him even more than he thought possible. It was a beautiful day.

Meanwhile, he, C, D, and the Pug were moving to a rental property—a visibly, from the exterior, rundown row house on an unpaved road in a down-on-its-heels section of what was chiefly an upscale neighborhood. He, however, was looking inward and the interior of the house (along with its two-car garage and the landlord's pet friendliness) closed the deal for him and the new life he envisioned for himself. Like the City house, it had four levels. Unlike the City house, it was light and bright and not overwhelming. It would be a better setting for a more calm and simplified life. He would take the smallest of the three bedrooms, and would sleep in a twin bed, which only became awkward when he started a relationship with the next-door neighbor, and he, C, and D would forge ahead. Just before the move, he commemorated the end and the beginning:

Dear A, B, C, and D—

As the year draws to a close and I reflect on it, on the past few years, and on leaving our home of the last 18 years, it is "goodbye to all that" and hello to what may come next. Regrets? Plenty. But even in carefully crafted lives, there are crosses to bear and crises to endure. How do we face them? Does any betterment come from them and, if so, do we embrace it? Or do we act the victim, become entitled, get bogged down in things we cannot control, embark on a road of bad behavior? This matters.

The crash and burn was waiting to happen, as was its ripple effect—the havoc wrought on your young lives. I see now that, in the days and months and years leading to it, I gave insufficient attention to what should have mattered most. I won't let myself off the hook, yet the upside was we met it head-on, we discovered reserves of inner strength and resilience, and we grew, learned, and made needed corrections. Who knows if this would have occurred in other circumstances.

Not that I have a choice, but it is onward and upward from here. And, at the risk of being delusional, I might even try to convince myself that "I am still big, it's the pictures that got small." Put in a different way, though the platform or the set may diminish, there is much to live for and there is much that brings joy—each of you.

My wish then is that the upcoming year and those that follow be peaceful, safe, and spiritual ones for each of you, and that you make and achieve goals, small and lofty, that will give meaning to your lives. You will each, doubtlessly, have your own version of the big life—of center stage. That, I suspect, will be a sustainable one and not a house of cards. Define and nurture it by good works, acts of kindness, mutual support, loving relations, temperance, and gratitude.

You keep me strong, I keep you strong.

Didi

CPSIA information can be obtained
at www.ICGtesting.com
Printed in the USA
BVHW071714070622
639117BV00004B/380